"Just imagine you two knowing each other!"

Vance was clearly amazed.

"We met in Cyprus," Alida heard Darius saying. "Eight years ago, at an engagement ceremony first and then later at a wedding." His face was a steely mask, giving away nothing of his feelings.

Alida, maintaining her dignity, said, "Yes, I remember very well, Mr. Valaris. The girl had been forced into marriage by her father. She was just seventeen and had seen the man only once before the wedding."

"Forced?" Vance echoed perplexedly. "Are you saying it was against her will?"

"Very much against her will," returned Alida. "The man saw her, desired her and offered for her. She was married to a stranger." Alida marveled at the cool, detached quality of her voice. No one would have believed she was talking about herself....

ANNE HAMPSON
is also the author of these

Harlequin Presents

and these

Harlequin Romances

Many of these titles are available at your local bookseller.

For a free catalogue listing all available Harlequin Romances
and Harlequin Presents, send your name and address to:

HARLEQUIN READER SERVICE
1440 South Priest Drive, Tempe, AZ 85281
Canadian address: Stratford, Ontario N5A 6W2

ANNE HAMPSON

bride for a night

Harlequin Books

TORONTO • LONDON • LOS ANGELES • AMSTERDAM
SYDNEY • HAMBURG • PARIS • STOCKHOLM • ATHENS • TOKYO

Harlequin Presents edition published November 1981.
ISBN 0-373-10463-4

Original hardcover edition published in 1979
by Mills & Boon Limited

CHAPTER ONE

FATHER and daughter faced one another, their eyes dark with anger.

"I won't be forced into an arranged marriage!" quivered Alida fiercely. "I'm not a Greek! My mother's English and I'd rather go to her than marry this man you've chosen for me—a man I've never even met!" Her English was excellent, but in the heat of her protests she had lapsed into Greek now and then.

"Your mother!" Marcos Palides spat out the words. "She deserted you when you were a baby. What makes you think she'll want you now?" Alida was silent, not knowing how to answer that. After only fifteen months of marriage her mother had decided she did not care either for her husband or for Cyprus and she had left one day when Marcos was at his office in Nicosia, left without a word of warning or regret. Alida was left with her aunt Sophia, who was still in Marcos's employ. "She's never wanted to know how you're getting on," continued Marcos bitterly. "The divorce—then her remarriage to one of her own kind! That's all I ever learned about her, and it's all I ever want to learn! Never mention her again, understand?"

Alida nodded. Here, in Cyprus, daughters never thought of disobeying their parents, hence her own despair on learning that a marriage had been arranged for her. She was trying to put up a fight, but hopelessness filled her heart.

"Father, I don't want to be married yet. I'm only seventeen—"

"It's old enough to be married." He raised a hand as she would have interrupted him. "You'll do as I say, Alida! I've done a lot of scheming to bring about this offer. Darius is wealthy in his own right; he'll be wealthier still when his father dies. And the old man's on his last legs; you know it. That's the reason why Darius is anxious to marry. His father wants to see another generation born, see an heir to the Valaris fortune—"

"Don't!" broke in Alida angrily. "I won't be treated like a Greek girl—married for the production of sons!" She turned away, unable to face her father's stern countenance. Her heart was heavy within her. She wanted to see something of life before settling down to the married state. In any case, she wanted to choose her own husband, to marry for love. Often she had wept bitter tears over her birth. She was half Greek Cypriot, and in addition under the sole control of her father. Why, oh, why had her English mother deserted her!

"There are many girls who would be happy to change places with you," said Marcos, ignoring her vehement words. "Rich husbands are not so easily found these days. He doesn't want a dowry, either, so that's another thing in his favour."

"He's too old for me!" The desperation in her voice was matched by the expression in her soft brown eyes. Her hands were clenched at her sides, clammily cold, as was her wide, intelligent forehead where beads of perspiration stood out among tendrils of gleaming dark hair. Her mouth trembled spasmodically, evidence of the tension within her. She had ideas of running away, but they were vague. She had no money at all, and no one to turn to in her misery.

"He's twenty-four. Seven years older than you. You're talking rubbish, Alida!" Inflexible the tone and hard the stare he directed toward her. He was an unfeeling man who had never sentimentalised over the wife who had given him a daughter instead of the son he had wanted. And, having committed the crime, she had deserted him shamefully, leaving her four-month-old daughter on his hands. She had previously asserted that she ought never to have married a foreigner. She had been swayed by the romantic situation which the holiday in Cyprus had provided; she and Marcos had met at a dance and within a month she was married to him. Alida had often wondered about her—about her looks and her character and her build, and there were times when she desperately wanted to meet her. If only she could go to England and find her. . . .

"What are you thinking about, Alida?" Her father's soft voice broke into her reverie and she looked at him. He was handsome still, and Alida thought that when he was young he could very easily have made her mother fall a victim to his charms.

"It's. . . nothing," she faltered, afraid to tell him the truth. "Father, I can't be expected to marry a man I've never met. Please don't make me—"

"I've given Darius my promise."

"I might hate him!" Alida's throat was dry, but she managed to add fiercely, "I *shall* hate him, for offering for me in the first place!"

"He saw you, and liked what he saw." Calm, unemotional words, and the dark eyes were glassy cold. "You'll be meeting him tomorrow evening, at your betrothal party. A week later you'll be married. It's custom, and you have always known it. This fuss must stop, Alida!'' The last sentence was spoken in Greek and Alida frowned. She preferred English, which was spoken freely throughout the island.

"I shall tell him I was coerced! I hope he'll be a gentleman and refuse to marry me under circumstances like those!''

"You will tell him no such thing,'' warned her father. "Remember, my girl, that here we school our errant daughters with the whip.''

"Not for speaking their minds, Father,'' she said. "Only for—for. . . .'' Her voice trailed to silence. She had heard of a girl being punished by her father for meeting a man secretly. The girl swore she had done no wrong, but the very fact of her being seen with the man was more than enough to bring down the terrible punishment on her head.

"Enough!'' Marcos's eyes narrowed threateningly. Alida, admitting she was beaten, bowed her head in a gesture of meekness and respect, but scalding tears were running down her cheeks. What could she do to save herself? If only she had some money. . . . She turned her head, hearing a footstep in the hall. Her aunt came into the room and, swift to see that something was wrong, looked enquiringly at her brother.

"Alida's rebelling against my authority,'' he snapped. "She doesn't want to marry Darius Valaris.'' He shrugged and gave a small sigh of impatience. "She doesn't know when she's lucky.''

"Stupid girl,'' chided the woman, catching some of her brother's impatience. "Darius will be a millionaire one day soon.''

"I don't care for his money, Aunt Sophia,'' cried

Alida. "I want to marry for love, like the English girls do!"

Her aunt came farther into the room, shaking her head. She was softer than her brother but was still of the opinion that Alida was doing exceedingly well for herself in having an offer from the wealthy Darius Valaris. She looked at her, noticing the wet cheeks, the clenched fists.

"You do realise that your beauty attracted him? You ought to be flattered."

"I'm not flattered! I hate him for offering for me!"

"How can you hate him when you've never even met him?"

Alida said nothing. What was the use? She would obey her father; there was nothing else she could do.

Her aunt was staring at her, the very dark eyes moving from her high forehead to her eyes, large and dark and filled with tears of despair.

"Perhaps," she sighed at length, "I ought not to have persuaded your father to let you attend the English school in Nicosia."

"I'm glad you did, Aunt Sophia. I'll always be grateful."

"She learned too much about England," snapped Marcos. "I can't think why I listened to you, Sophia."

Alida turned away from her father's gaze. She had spoken the truth when she said she would always be grateful to her aunt. At the English school she had been able to perfect her mother's language; she had met English girls, daughters of certain officials who were working in Cyprus, and through them had learned a great deal about England and the freedom with which young people were allowed to go about together. She longed to visit the country, to compare it with Cyprus, which she loved, despite the restrictions its custom imposed upon her. It was only since her father had mentioned, some months ago, that she must marry soon, that she had become unhappy, yearning for the chance to spread her wings before settling down to the restrictive existence of married life.

"You'll be happy enough, child, when the babies start coming," Aunt Sophia was saying in an attempt to comfort her niece, but Alida shuddered visibly. To bear children to a man she did not love!

"I wish I were dead!" she cried, looking pleadingly at her aunt. "Help me. . . dear Aunt Sophia, help me!"

"Go to your room!" ordered Marcos, pointing to the door. "I've had enough of this nonsense! You will marry the man I've chosen, just as every other girl marries the man her parents choose for her!"

She went to the church dressed in white—in a fairytale gown of satin and lace, with a veil and orange-blossom. Her delicate features were set and still, like a statue's; she never turned to glance at the man at her side, the tall, swarthy-skinned Greek with the raven hair and black, piercing eyes that seemed to look right into her very soul, the man who, having seen her, had offered for her in the traditional Greek way, uncaring for her feelings, indifferent to the fact that the idea of marriage to him would be abhorrent to her. His father had begged him to have an heir; he had agreed because of his deep love for the old man who was dying, slowly and in great pain. Alida was to bring him happiness by producing the child he wanted. It seemed incredible that Darius had not sensed her misery, she thought, as she stood by his side at the altar and listened to the black-bearded priest droning away in Greek. Never, she decided, had a bride felt as desolate as she.

It was a fashionable wedding, very different from the typical village wedding where the feast was set out in the sunshine, usually on land brought by the bride as part of her *prika*. The banquet was held at the Hilton in Nicosia, with everything correct, the guests being rich and influential, like the bridegroom. The honeymoon was to be in Athens. Darius had made all the arrangements including getting Alida a passport. This, and her suitcases, were in the room upstairs, where she and Darius were spending the first night. Tomorrow afternoon they would fly to Athens and stay for a fortnight before returning to Cyprus to live in the beautiful white villa overlooking the sea at Paphos.

Alida, silent, and pale as a lily, scarcely moved her eyes as she entered the room where the banquet was set out. She sat beside her stranger bridegroom, answering his questions in monosyllables, coldly and without expression. Her manner began to anger him and she noticed the harshness of the pagan-like features. She cared nothing for his feelings; she hoped he was unhappy, hoped that already he was beginning to regret making the offer for her. He knew she was half English and therefore would probably resent an arranged marriage. She posed for guests wanting pictures, but never smiled as she stood beside her bridegroom, fragile and feminine and exquisitely beautiful—but not radiantly so, as she had always imagined she would be on her wedding day.

The banquet was over at last and some of the guests began to leave. But one or two others stepped forward to pin money on Alida's dress. The custom was always followed in the village weddings, where both bride and groom had paper money pinned to their clothes. But with fashionable weddings this custom had almost died out...almost.... Alida glanced down. One note was no less than a hundred Cyprus pounds, and several more were fifty-pound notes.... Money....Alida's heart leapt within her, then pounded wildly as the idea came to her. Money.... Enough and more to get her to England.

Darius came forward and lifted an arrogant hand, putting an instant stop to the pinning on of the money. Alida felt that she hated him with a black venom! Yet there was enough, she told herself again.

The bridal suite was in white, with every luxury possible. Alida stood in the middle of the bedroom floor and glanced all around. She was still in her wedding-dress, having dutifully stayed until the last of the guests had gone. There had been dancing, and drinking, and laughter. The guests had left by degrees as soon as the banquet was over, but many had stayed on until after midnight. She suspected that jokes had passed between the men and she hated them all—every single guest except the few English girls whom she herself had invited.

She swung round as her husband came in and closed the door behind him. She looked at him, staggered by the fact that she had not yet really examined his looks, or noticed that his physique was perfect. Taller than most Greeks, he was slender as well, with wide shoulders and narrow waist and hips. His suit fitted to perfection; his shirt glowed white against his tawny throat. He looked older than his twenty-four years, and yet the smile that came slowly gave him an almost boyish look.

His smile died as she turned from him and she sensed a wave of anger spreading over him. Greek men were not used to being treated with this kind of haughty indifference by their womenfolk.

"Turn around." Soft the tone, but dangerous, with a shade of warning in its depths. Alida obeyed him, lifting anguished eyes to his mask-like face. She saw the tautness of the jaw, the compression of the lips that were normally sensuous, like those of most Greek men. Her glance strayed to the high cheekbones that stood prominently above the hollows of his cheeks. Formidable, he was, and very frightening.

His hands came out in a sort of imperious, commanding gesture; she placed hers within his palms, then shuddered as he brought her to him, his arms about her strong and possessive, his body hard, like iron. She twisted from him instinctively and said in pleading desperation,

"Don't...I haven't had the chance to get to know you! Please leave me alone tonight—leave me, I say!"

The dark foreign eyes glittered and despair closed around her heart. He would take her no matter how much she pleaded. He would show her that he was her master now, and teach her that she must always remember it. Once again she cried in anguish, "Why did my mother desert me!" She felt instinctively that her attitude astonished him, since he had taken it for granted that she was inwardly grateful for having managed to win a husband of his wealth and standing.

"You're asking me to leave you, on our wedding night?" His straight black brows were lifted a fraction. "You're being absurd, Alida."

"I don't know you!" she cried. "I was coerced into this marriage—into marriage with a stranger! Have you no pity for me, no understanding of my feelings?" Her eyes were bright with unshed tears; her voice quivered on a gentle, pleading note as she added, "I beg of you, Darius—give me a little time to get to know you. I will try, I promise, not to take too long...." Her voice trailed to a despairing silence. What was the use of this humility? Darius was hard, like her father, like most Greek men. She thought suddenly of the money which she had unpinned from her dress and put into the tight cuff of her sleeve. She could feel its crispness, and the faint discomfort of the new notes against her skin. She was careful not to let it rustle lest her husband should hear, and take it from her.

An ugly light had come into his eyes. He had been watchful all the time—throughout the ceremony and the banquet afterward—and Alida knew he had never been under any illusions about the feelings she had tried to hide beneath her rigid features. But in his arrogance he had not expected to encounter any resistance. Women here were meek; they had been taught to be so from birth, and so he had fully expected his young bride to come to him willingly and obediently, ready to lose her virginal state in total submission to his will. Instead, she was standing erect, icily unresponsive, her face tautly pale but with her dark eyes burning with what could only be described as hatred.

Darius had lived all his life in Cyprus; he had been brought up to consider his sex as supreme, so superior that they might have been gods and their womenfolk mere mortals to be subjugated. Alida supposed it was a chastening experience for him to have her stand out against him. But as she watched his expression she knew that he was in authority over her. He was piqued, she thought, and furiously angry.

"Come here," he ordered brusquely, and pointed to a spot close to his feet. Alida shook her head, her heart pounding so violently that she felt physically sick.

"I d-don't w-want—!" She got no further. Her husband's hand shot out and gripped her wrist. She gasped with pain as his iron-hard grasp tightened and he pulled her roughly toward him. His hold was hawser-strong, his mouth hard and ruthless against her gentle, unresponsive lips. Her immobility infuriated him; he had had many pillow-friends and never had one been able to hold out against his ardour. All the pagan qualities of his forebears were brought into evidence as, with the arrogance of a conqueror, he set about subjugating her completely. She gave a little moan. The blood was rushing to her temples; every nerve and sense were dissolving in the whirlpool of his passion. Fear suffocated her... fear of the unknown. When for a few seconds he drew his mouth from hers she looked up at him through scalding tears and begged him to let her go. His eyes marked the brightness of her own, but no vestige of pity was awakened in him.

"Get undressed!" he ordered, his glance raking her body. "Or perhaps you'd like me to do it for you?"

She shook her head dumbly. Words would not come through the blockage of fear and misery in her throat. Her heart was still throbbing wildly, but in contrast the rest of her body seemed nerveless, numbed by her terrible fear. He swung her round with a swift, imperious movement and unzipped the lovely dress. It fell to the floor and she held her breath as she thought of the money hidden in the sleeve. But she thought too of her slender body exposed to his lecherous gaze and bent to pick up the dress again. He was before her; a command and she was obediently stepping out of it, and he flung it on to a chair. Fascinated, she watched one sleeve fall over the edge and come to rest on the floor. The money was in the other sleeve. . . .

Darius was staring at her, then his eyes moved to her dainty ankles, then upward slowly to the tender places and her tiny waist. Stepping forward, he took her in his arms; she stiffened involuntarily, an action which seemed to ignite his fury once again. She knew his ego had been deflated but could not accept this as an excuse for the cruelty he showed on forcing her lips apart, crushing her mouth, kissing her without respect, exerting all the brutality that would have been characteristic of his pagan ancestors. His tongue explored inside her tender lips, sensuous and provocative. There was another rush of blood to her temples as his ardour increased, and then she actually knew the awareness of desire as he held her breast with the hand of ruthless domination. How typically Greek he was! Her supple young body was against his, so close that she felt the sickening sensation of its hard virility against her stomach. She wanted to cry out for help, to scream so loudly that some of the hotel staff would hear, and come to see what was wrong. But her mouth was possessed again, and she went limp. His lovemaking was gradually eliciting a response; her throat grew dry as shame enveloped her. There would be no escape tonight. . . but tomorrow. . . . Yes, she had money and a passport. She was determined to make a bid for escape tomorrow.

"You're beautiful!" Darius breathed hoarsely, his sensuous mouth exploring the tender curves of her breast through the fine lace bra she wore. "God, but you're desirable! I knew what you would be like in bed, though, knew it the moment I set eyes on you. I was so sure you'd be the right wife for me!"

"Desire!" she flared, managing to step back as his

hold upon her slackened. "That's all you wanted me for—the satisfying of your desires!"

He stared, eyes glinting and narrowed.

"What else does one marry for?" he wanted to know.

Alida's lip curled contemptuously.

"There does happen to be such a thing as love," she said. "Love between a man and a woman."

"Love?" Her husband appeared to find this rather amusing. "Females talk of such things—" A sudden laugh escaped him, grating on her nerve-ends. "What is love but sex?"

She coloured at the word. It was the first time she had heard it from the lips of a man. She and her school-friends had talked about it; but at home.... Why, her father would have slapped her across the face if she had spoken the forbidden word in his house. He himself had always been guarded in his speech; to say that Alida had been strictly nurtured would have been putting it very mildly indeed.

"Love," she said tremulously, "is to do with other things."

"Such as?" The black eyes raked her near-naked body and she saw impatience in their depths.

"The spiritual and the mental. Two people can love each other dearly even without sex."

"Rubbish! As for love being spiritual—you're talking about the Church, and God."

"No, I'm not." Her eyes searched around for some covering for her body. Her negligé was on the bed, but Darius was in the way and she dared not reach for it. "Between a man and a woman there can be spiritual love, and that's what I want when I marry—" She stopped, her mouth still open. "I mean—"

"Yes," softly and dangerously, "just what do you

mean?'' Alida closed her mouth, shaking her head.
''Don't get any ideas of following your mother's exam-
ple,'' he went on in the same soft tone of voice. ''You're
mine now, for all time, and don't you ever forget it,
because if you do you'll wish you'd never been born.''

She shivered, icy cold from head to foot. Again she
glanced at her negligé, but Darius was moving and within seconds she was being swept once again into the
vortex of his unbridled passion. His hands sought and
fondled, his pagan lips possessed with an ardour that
sent a quiver of excitement through her body. She felt
herself lifted from her feet, carried across the room and
laid on the bed. Her head fell into the pillow as she
resigned herself to the inevitable. But deep within her
mind her one fierce resolve remained rooted. She would
escape no matter what his threats. She would fly to
England, seek a divorce like her mother had done, and
then, one day, she would marry an Englishman, a man
who would love her dearly, just as she would love him.

Darius left her and went to the bathroom, returning
quickly clad in a black dressing-gown. Alida could smell
body lotion and despite herself she liked it. She had got
into bed; he dropped the gown and slid in beside her.
For a long while she remained impassive, conscious of
the gradual increase of his anger. But eventually his
powers of persuasion began to efface rational thought
and her mouth and body relaxed in a submission that
was voluntary. And she heard his triumphant laugh
when presently her soft young body quivered with desire
for him. The change in her seemed to bring about a
change in him; his caresses were less rough, and it was
with a sort of savage gentleness that he made love to
her, firing every nerve in her body so that she felt no
resentment at her newly-awakened emotions. On the

contrary, she derived sublime fulfillment in responding to his ardent and masterful possession of her body.

A long while later, after the ragged nerve-settlings of spent emotion, she lay within the circle of his arm, one of her own arms thrown across his naked frame. And her eyes closed eventually and she fell into a quiet, dreamless sleep.

The morning sun was bright as she drew back the curtains and looked out on to waving palms and bougainvilleas and flaring crimson hibiscus. The world looked so wonderful.... Her husband still slept; she moved over to where her wedding-dress lay on the chair and silently extracted the money from within the sleeve. She gasped as she counted more than five hundred pounds. Two notes alone were each for one hundred Cyprus pounds, and the others were all for fifty pounds. The guests at village weddings usually gave five pounds at the most, but of course no guest at a society wedding like that of Darius and his bride would give anything less than fifty pounds.

The possession of all that money gave her a confidence she had never known in her life before. She would find her mother; she had no idea how she would go about it, but her resolve was so firm that she found it impossible even to visualise failure. Fortunately she had something to go on. She had once heard her father mention her mother's maiden name when he was talking to her Aunt Sophia—Mountchesney. Alida had not realised that it was a most uncommon name until having mentioned it to her English friends at school, she had been told that none of them had ever heard of it. Alida now felt that she would at least be able to trace some of her mother's family and, through them, she would find her mother.

She had heard of an English radio programme called "Where Are You Now?" in which lost relatives were often traced, and she decided to make an attempt to have her enquiry broadcast. However, in the main, her plans were vague. She knew she would be able to think more clearly once she had escaped from her husband and landed safely in England, where she would book in at an hotel. That was the most important move; after that she could set about finding her mother. How little those people who had pinned money on her knew for what purpose it would be used, she thought, dropping it into her bag.

She swung around as her husband stirred. He stared at her uncomprehendingly for a second, then smiled at her across the room. She managed a thin response, scared suddenly of giving herself away. He must not suspect! She felt sure he would somehow manage to keep her a prisoner if he did.

"Did you sleep well?" The prosaic question released the tautness of her nerves and her smile deepened.

"Very well, thank you."

"Come here."

She stood irresolute, hating the idea of a delay in her plan to get away. She wanted to escape while Darius was in the bath, to get away before breakfast, even.

"I—er—want to—to have my bath," she stammered, but he interrupted her with an imperious gesture, his voice changing dramatically at the same time, to one of stern command.

"I said come here! You'll learn to obey me, Alida, at once!"

Prudently she did as she was told, reflecting bitterly that she had learned obedience from the cradle, ever conscious of the superiority of her father, and in fact, of all males, be they fathers, brothers or husbands. It was not like this in England; there was equality of the sexes, she had been assured by her school-friends. Alida had often thought how wonderful it would be to discuss plans with one's husband instead of listening meekly to him making them. There was a lovely sort of comradeship in that kind of union of which women of the East had no knowledge at all.

Darius waited as she approached the bed slowly, then he pulled her down as she reached it, swinging her across him, turning her as he did so, and pressed his lips to hers. Instinctively she struggled when he began to make love to her, but his strength made her puny efforts appear ridiculous and she eventually gave in to him, all the while hating his power over her, hating the man he was and would always be.

It seemed an age before he let her go; she rose dizzily and went to the bathroom. She felt better when she had bathed, felt cleaner, having washed her body of the contamination of a contact she did not want.

The money, and the passport, were already in her handbag, and when Darius eventually went into the bathroom she hastily packed a small suitcase with the essentials necessary for the stay in an hotel and before her husband was out of the bath she was gone. She heard him splashing as she opened the bedroom door and went through into the sitting-room of the suite. From there she stepped quietly into the corridor and ran for the lift. The ground floor was reached; a taxi stood at the entrance and she got into it.

"Limassol," she said breathlessly. "I'm in a great hurry! I have to catch a boat."

"Very good."

At Limassol she paid him off and watched him drive

away from the dock. Another taxi was called, this time to take her back to Nicosia, where she alighted and immediately took another, this time to the airport. She enquired about flights to England, fully expecting to have to hide somewhere until she could get a flight. But to her surprise there happened to be a flight to Athens within an hour and there was a seat available. She could get a quick connection from Athens to London, she was told, her informant appearing to be optimistic about her managing to get a seat on this other plane.

Fear was heavy within her during the hour's wait, but she hoped she had covered her tracks well enough to put her husband off the idea that she might be at the airport. If he did happen to be lucky enough to speak to the first taximan he would be told she had gone to Limassol to catch a boat. There might not be a boat that day, and Darius could of course know this, but nevertheless he would surely go to Limassol, seeing that this was where she had gone.

At last she was on the plane, but it was only when it was actually taking off that Alida was able to breathe freely. She was free! What would her father think? It was his own fault for forcing her into a marriage she did not want. Aunt Sophia would be vexed, but Alida did not think she would be all that ready to condemn her niece. She had always been rather more tolerant than her brother, allowing for the fact that Alida was half English.

Alida's thoughts flitted here and there, one moment on her husband and the next on her father. Then she would think about all her husband's friends, and of the humiliation he would suffer when it was learned that his wife had left him after less than a day of marriage. She thought of his father, who was in effect the cause of it all. He would not be happy, but that did not trouble Alida in the least. Why should she worry herself over a man she had never even met?

What would her mother be like? Would she be ready to welcome into her home the child she had deserted as a baby? Well, if she decided to turn her daughter away Alida would still remain in England. She would get a job—domestic work, since that was all she could do; but it was better than being a slave to a man she did not love, whose only reason for marrying her was to make his father happy.

At last the plane touched down at Athens and the first part of her journey was over. And then she was landing in London and excitement was high within her. She went through Customs with her one small suitcase. All her Cyprus money was in her bag and she did not know that she could have changed some of it at the airport. She would change it at the bank in London tomorrow morning, she thought, very thankful indeed for the things she had learned from the English girls at school.

She felt exhilarated as she left the airport. Free! For the very first time in her life! She wanted to sing, to dance along instead of walking sedately, trying to look as if she were used to airports and travelling. A taxi took her to a small hotel in Earl's Court which the driver recommended. He chatted for a few minutes, asking if she were on holiday. She said no, said that she was visiting relatives, and then she instantly changed the subject in case he should want to know why she was wanting an hotel. She looked out, at all the hustle and bustle of the city. Her friends had tried to describe London to her, but it was far more crowded than she had expected. However, Earl's Court was quieter, and the hotel faced a square where trees swayed in the sunshine. She used the only English money she had with her to pay for the taxi.

The smallness of the hotel was suited to her mood and to her pocket, for she was wise enough to know that she had to be careful, since she had no idea how long it would take to find her mother. She had married again, but from something her aunt had once let fall Alida gathered that her second husband was dead. So unless her mother had married for a third time she was a widow. If so, she would most likely be very happy at having her long-lost daughter living with her.

However, the fact had to be faced that it might take a long time to trace her, in which case Alida had to be careful of her expenses.

The room was small and spotlessly clean and Alida felt at home in it. A maid carried her suitcase—although she would rather have carried it herself—and stayed in the room looking expectant. Alida had to apologise for having no English money, but promised her a tip in the morning when she had been to the bank.

Later, having had dinner at the hotel, she went to her room. She felt lost and lonely and a long way from home. Her buoyancy had left her; she felt flat and hopeless and it was only with the greatest difficulty that she prevented herself from finding relief in tears. She must keep her chin up, she told herself sternly. One day she would be able to laugh at her dejection... one day in the future when she had learned to be English, had acquired confidence and self-assurance like the girls she had met at school.

A night's sleep restored her courage, and she rose feeling ready for anything. Her first enquiry was made at the hotel desk where she happened to catch the manager as he was having a few words with the reception clerk. He listened as she said she was anxious to find some relatives by the name of Mountchesney. Could he tell her how to go about it? She knew of the radio programme and would like to know how she could get on to it.

"You write in," he told her, "giving as much information as you can. In your case you'd mention the name, and say something about these relatives—whether they'd always lived in England—or wherever it is they do live...." He tailed off as Alida nodded. She was about to say that she knew nothing at all about these relatives—in fact it struck her that her mother might not have any relatives—but she refrained, and a short while later she was in her room again, writing a letter to the B.B.C., to the man who produced the programme. The manager had also given her the address of the nearest Citizens' Advice Bureau and after posting her letter she caught the bus he had recommended and was on her way. The people at the Bureau were helpful only in that they advised her to advertise in the Personal column of *The Times*, which she did without any further waste of time, inserting the advertisement for three days initially as advised by the counter clerk. If she had no replies then she could insert it again.

She came out of the office feeling even more optimistic than she had that morning, for something told her that it would not be very long at all before she was in touch with her mother.

CHAPTER TWO

ALTHOUGH Alida had hoped her mother would welcome her into her home, she had not for one moment expected to meet with such a warm reception as the one she had received.

The reunion had come about through the radio programme, when she had received not only one but several letters, all from relatives of Alida's mother. Alida learned that she had two aunts and an uncle, with four cousins in addition.

And if that was not enough, her mother was engaged to a charming man who showed the same delight at the reunion as did the mother and daughter, his fiancée having mentioned to him that she had a daughter whom she had left with her father in Cyprus. Roger Waltham had met Margaret Blane on a cruise ship in the Caribbean and they had become engaged before the cruise was ended. He was from America, in big business, and it had been agreed that his fiancée would live over there when they were married. But for the present they were together only at intervals, Roger coming over to England every two months or so. To Alida it seemed a rather strange arrangement, but her mother explained that she was not impatient for marriage as she had been a widow so long that she was thoroughly used to her freedom.

"We shall marry in a year or so," she told Alida casually. "Roger might decide to retire then and sell the business to a friend of his."

Alida, having been comfortably settled in her mother's delightfully converted cottage in the grounds of Vale Royal Abbey in Cheshire for almost a fortnight leant back in her chair and gave a contented sigh.

"I still can't believe that I found you so easily, and so quickly, Mother...." The name rolled from her tongue with the same tingle of pleasure as on the first time she had ever used it. Mother.... She had a mother of her very own, a mother who had been delighted with her beautiful daughter. Alida looked at her, a pretty woman of thirty-eight, with auburn hair and grey-green eyes. Her features were strong, except for a hint of weakness in the chin. They did not in any way resemble those of her daughter, since Alida had all the classical firmness and beauty of her Greek ancestors. Her hair was very dark brown, but it did have auburn lights and it curled naturally, like her mother's. Her eyes were large and widely-spaced and framed enchantingly by thick curling lashes. Her forehead was wide, as was her mother's, her mouth full and generous. Her mother had been horrified that "such a baby" had been forced into marriage and assured Alida that it could be dissolved eventually.

"I know how you feel, darling," said Mrs. Blane affectionately. "I myself was staggered to receive a phone call from my sister saying she had heard our name on the radio and that a girl from Cyprus was seeking her mother. From the other information given there was no doubt at all in my mind that it was my daughter who was here, in England, looking for me." She smiled and shook her head, a gesture of faint regret. "I often thought of you, darling, but believe me, life with your father was not pleasant from the first. Men from the

East are too passionate—but not only that, they have no finesse in their lovemaking. It's a case of 'let's have a baby' and they just get on with it—'' She broke off, laughing a little. "I'm embarrassing you, darling, aren't I? Sorry, dear. But you did have one night with a Greek, so you must know what I mean.''

Alida nodded her head.

"They're like savages,'' she murmured reflectively, repressing a shudder. "Oh, but it's wonderful to have escaped from him! You don't suppose he could come here and make me return to him, do you?'' she added anxiously.

"Never!'' declared her mother vehemently, her eyes sparkling. "You're free now, my love, and you stay that way!''

Protection. It was wonderful to have someone to rely on, to care for you and guard you against a man like Darius Valaris. Let him marry one of his own kind if he wanted to have children.

"How long will it be before I can get a divorce?'' she asked, her eyes wandering to the latticed window through which she could see the green undulating grounds of the Abbey. It was unoccupied at present, but in the grounds there were the old cottages of the servants. These had all been sold and their purchasers had renovated them without taking away any of their old world character. There were landscaped gardens where once there had been the servants' allotments or kitchen plots; garages had been built to house the gracious cars which the owners now possessed. As Alida looked out at another cottage, white in the sunshine and with a glorious array of flowers in the garden, she found herself trying to visualise what this little community was like in olden times. But her visions always included such things as she would see in Cyprus and she gave a small sigh at knowing so little about her mother's country. She almost said, "I wish you'd taken me with you, Mother," but of course she refrained, managing to stem the words in time. Her relationship with her mother was all she could have desired and she did not intend to do or say anything that might in any way impair it. Love was not there yet, but affection and gratitude were. Alida felt sure that love would come to her eventually.

"Well," answered Mrs. Blane, "here, we have to wait two years before we can start divorce proceedings, but with your being married in Cyprus it might be different." She pursed her lips thoughtfully. "We shall have to make some enquiries, love. Leave it all to me; I'll have you free as soon as ever I can." She smiled at Alida across the pretty, oak-beamed sitting-room. "We'll find you a nice English boy—a rich one, of course. You don't want to spend your life washing and ironing and cooking and cleaning. At least your father was reasonably well off— This Darius was a millionaire, you said?" she added with a touch of interest.

"He isn't yet, but he's very rich. He owns vast areas of orange groves near Famagusta. His father's wealthy and he's got an incurable disease—I did tell you?" Alida looked enquiringly at her mother, who nodded her head, and Alida went on, "Darius is his only son— his only child, in fact, so he'll come into everything within the next year or so."

"I can see why your father was so keen for you to marry him. A rich husband for one's daughter is the dream of every Cypriot father." Mrs. Blane paused a moment. "I might ask you about him eventually, but for the present—well, I'm just too thrilled at having you and all I want is to show you off! Tomorrow we'll go

and visit my sister—the one who first heard the programme and rang me. She and her family were going on
holiday the following day. They've come back now, so
we shall visit them tomorrow.''

''Where do they live?''

''In Chester. You haven't been there yet—oh, there is
so much for us to do, my love! Roger'll be going away
in about two weeks, so we shall have each other to ourselves. Won't that be marvellous?''

Alida nodded her dark head. She was happy and it
showed, in the brightness of her eyes, in her lovely smile
which was—although she did not know it—what first
attracted the attention of the man who had become her
husband.

''I'm dying to see Aunt Lucie, and her daughter—
Marcelle, I think you said?''

Her mother nodded, but there was a strange frown on
her forehead which Alida could not fail to notice.

''You'll like Aunt Lucie, but Marcelle's a rather odd
sort of girl. Her character's conflicting because she can
be charming one day and quite catty the next.'' She
looked at her daughter, her grey-green eyes flickering
from her slender ankles to her shapely legs and then up
to her waist before eventually coming to rest on her
lovely face. ''I'm half afraid she'll be jealous of you,
love. You see, it's always been accepted that she's the
great beauty of the family.''

''I'm sure she won't be jealous of me,'' said Alida,
flushing at her mother's words. ''I'm not really beautiful—''

''But you are, child,'' interrupted her mother. ''Surely you know it!''

''Darius said so,'' mused Alida, not in the least having intended to bring her husband into it.

"Obviously he would think so," returned her mother. "A man in his position would never offer for a plain girl. You were something quite special in his eyes." She paused a moment, and her own eyes glinted with interest. "I'd like to have met him, I think. Despite the way I feel about him I'm sure he's an interesting character. Twenty-four, you said? He sounds older, but these Greek men *are* older. I found it so with your father." Another pause and then, thoughtfully, "I must confess that I liked some of the older Greek men. Perhaps Darius will become quite attractive in a few years' time."

"He's attractive already, Mother. It's just that I didn't love him, and also I resented his offering for me, just as if I were an ordinary Cypriot girl who would expect to have her marriage arranged for her."

Her mother nodded understandingly.

"He ought to have had more sense. But I do think he might change with age; he might come to realise that he should have treated you differently—made a different approach, I mean. If he had you might have adopted an attitude that would have ended in a love affair—"

"Never! I hated his way with me! He was rough and—and—" Alida could not go on because the memory sickened her. Mrs. Blane said soothingly,

"Forget it, darling, it's all in the past and you're no worse off for it. You've a happy future in front of you. Love will come one day and you shall have a proper wedding, not like that one where your heart was breaking."

Alida swallowed. Her wedding day.... The lovely dress that was so expensive, bought in Nicosia but made in Paris. The handsome bridegroom, the fashionable guests.... How wonderful it could have been! Alida

decided that when eventually she did marry an Englishman she would have a simple, quiet wedding, for she
felt she could not wear white again...and orange blos-
som for purity.

The following afternoon her mother drove the smart
sports car into Chester. Her mother's sister's house was
approached along an avenue of lime trees and as the car
bowled along it two collie dogs came bounding out from
somewhere at the back of the house. Alida liked the red
bricks, the black and white paint, the studded oaken
door. It was all so different from her Cyprus village,
where the villas were white and blue, with hibiscus and
oleanders, lovely poinsettias and jacarandas. Here, the
flowers were roses, in beds with paving stones in between, nemesias, forget-me-nots.... Yes, everything
was different.

Aunt Lucie was an effusive woman, ten years her sister's senior. Her hair was greying; her skin had a sallow
tint that seemed to emphasise the lines running out from
her eyes and those spreading along the sides of her
mouth. But what she lacked in appearance she more
than made up for in her manner and the gentle quietness
of her very attractive voice. Rather plumper than her
sylph-like sister, she was also taller and larger-boned.
Her greeting to Alida was welcoming and sincere. She
commented on her looks, her figure, and said finally
that although she was dark-haired and dark-eyed her
skin was so fair that no one would take her for anything
but English.

This pleased Alida and she gave her aunt one of her
beautiful smiles. They had entered a gracious living-
room through an equally gracious hall. Outside the sun
was hot, but in the house there was a fresh coolness that

was exceedingly pleasant to Alida, who had wondered at first if she would feel cold in the English climate. The weather was particularly warm, she had been told by her mother. She could certainly find it cold later, when autumn came along to replace summer.

"Marcelle's at work," Aunt Lucie said after she had put the kettle on to make the tea. "She's in a solicitor's office, but she has Wednesday afternoon off because they all work on Saturday mornings. She'll be here in about half an hour," she ended, glancing at the clock on the wall.

"How old is she?" asked Alida shyly.

"Twenty—well, not far off twenty-one."

"She's been engaged," interposed Margaret, "but it was broken off by mutual consent."

"Marcelle's hard to please, I'm afraid," admitted Lucie with a small sigh. "She favours the tall, dark handsome type—the kind you rarely come across in real life. She was keen on an Italian at one time. Then after she'd been on holiday in Spain she decided that a Spaniard would suit her very well—" Aunt Lucie broke off and shrugged her shoulders. "I often think she'll never marry at all." She looked at Alida and a smile came at once to her lips. "You, child, won't be so difficult to please when the time comes. But that time isn't yet. Enjoy yourself first."

"She will," stated Margaret emphatically. She glanced at Alida. She had decided that she would gain nothing by letting the family know that Alida had been married. The divorce would go through quietly, without fuss, and no one need ever know that Alida had been forced into a marriage she did not want. Margaret had explained her daughter's presence by saying that when Alida's father had tried to force her into marriage she had decided to come to England, and in the end she had been able to gain her father's approval and consent.

"I expect you're looking forward to being taken around by your mother?"

"Yes, I am," returned Alida enthusiastically. "I'd like to get married one day, but I want some fun first!"

Her aunt laughed, yet there was a strange little note of compassion and anxiety in her voice as she said,

"I hope all your wishes come true, dear. It's understandable that you should want to come here, but it's a very different world from the one you've been brought up in. Here we're always in a hurry, rushing about without quite knowing where we're going or what our aim is. From what I can gather Cyprus has a slower pace of life; the values are different—" She spread her hands deprecatingly. "I'm only going on what I've read, and things your mother's mentioned. It must be a very beautiful island."

"It is—very beautiful indeed." Alida thought of the scenery—the hills and valleys, the pine-clad slopes, and the glorious sea that lapped the beaches of pure white sand where palm trees swayed in the breeze and little children played naked on the shore. She had known that she would miss a great deal that was Cyprus, but freedom was all-important, and she would never have known freedom if she had remained in Cyprus as the wife of the arrogant and domineering Darius Valaris. If she could have chosen her own husband, then she felt she would never have wanted to leave the island, because she had always loved it—the scenery and the people.

"You'll be going back to visit your father, I expect?"

"Oh, yes," said Margaret before Alida could speak. "She isn't intending to make a clean break with her father, are you, my love?"

Alida shook her head, accepting the cue and relieved that her mother had answered for her.

"No...of course not."

"He'll miss you, after having you with him for so long."

"Er—yes, I suppose he will."

The conversation veered after that, mainly owing to Margaret's abrupt changing of the subject. Lucie went off after a while and returned with the tea-tray. She had been thinking, she said, that it would be a good idea to give a party for Alida, perhaps at the Grosvenor Hotel at Chester. It would get her into the swim of things; she would meet some young people.

"Marcelle would bring a few of her friends, and Joan and Mary would bring theirs. David, her other cousin, might condescend to come, but you know what he is— too full of his sailing these days to do much else. I believe he's off to Wales next week for a fortnight, but I'm not sure."

Alida sipped her tea and listened intently to the older women discussing the party. She had met Joan and Mary, daughters of Phyllis, her mother's other sister, but she had not met David, who was an orphan and lived in a flat which he shared with another young man. Aunt Phyllis was a widow, and worked in a large store in Chester, being the buyer in the fashion department. Alida's only uncle was Fred, Lucie's husband. He was bald and stout and jovial, Alida had learned, but she had not met him yet. She liked all the relations she had met. There was Marcelle and there was David. She hoped she would like them, but she did wonder about Marcelle, who seemed rather haughty and full of her own importance, and was the accepted beauty of the whole family.

It was decided to hold the party a fortnight hence, at the Grosvenor Hotel. The decision had just been finally made when the door opened and in walked Marcelle looking smart and thoroughly immaculate in a leaf green suit with a white blouse beneath it. Her shoes were expensive and matched the handbag she carried. Alida, in a flowered cotton dress and open-toed sandals, felt shabby suddenly, and inadequate.

"I saw Aunt Margaret's car, so I knew you'd arrived." Marcelle advanced slowly and gracefully into the room, her hips swaying, her pale blonde hair, with not so much as a strand out of place, taken back against her head in a french plait. Her glance swept around swiftly before coming to rest on Alida's face. The girl seemed to give a slight start, and her eyes, vivid blue and cold, narrowed slightly as if to match the sudden compression of her mouth. But the impression which Alida had was only fleeting; Marcelle's smile came through and she extended her hand towards her newly-found cousin.

"You're Alida! How very nice to meet you! We knew about you, of course, but you were always a vague, almost nebulous person whom we never expected to see. How are you liking England?"

"It's wonderful." Alida's voice was low and shy; she felt overwhelmed by the sheer self-confidence of the girl. Even the English girls at school had not been as poised and sure of themselves as Marcelle. The two older women were looking on, and then for a moment their eyes met. Lucie was under no illusions about her daughter and she, like Margaret, had already wondered about Marcelle's reaction to the entry into the family of a girl as beautiful as Alida.

"We're giving as party for Alida," said Margaret,

breaking the awkward little silence that had followed
her daughter's brief and timid response to Marcelle's
query. "We think the Grosvenor will be the best place.
It's central enough for all of us to get to without too
much trouble."

"A party?" Marcelle dropped her handbag on to a
chair and began to unbutton her jacket. "That'll be
nice. Who's coming?"

"We're inviting as many people as possible," answered her mother. "It's the only way of getting Alida
in the swim, as it were. She knows no one at present—
except for the family, of course."

Marcelle nodded, her blue eyes wandering again to
where Alida sat, on a low armchair by the window.

"You haven't met David yet, have you?"

"No, not yet." Alida was frowning inwardly. She
wondered if she imagined it or was there a strange, unfathomable inflection in her cousin's voice?

"David's handsome and rich and unattached," put in
Margaret, her glance straying to her niece who, having
taken off her jacket, was about to take possession of a
chair opposite to Alida. "He's not a first cousin," she
told her daughter, "although we seem always to look
upon him as first cousin to Marcelle and Mary and
Joan. I know I always feel I'm his real aunt."

"So do I," responded her sister with a reflective
smile. "But in actual fact he's a second cousin. However, that's not important. What is important is that we
make him come to the party. He knows so many nice
young men and he can bring them all along too."

Margaret was looking at her watch.

"I think it's time we were going, Lucie. I'm taking
Alida to Manchester this evening to dine at the Midland
and then we're going on to the show at the Palace. I've

heard it's the best they've had for years.'' She rose as she spoke and Alida followed suit. She felt more than ever inadequate beside her cousin, dressed as she was in what could only be described as a little girl dress. It was short and sleeveless, with a modest neckline and very little shape to the bodice. Her Aunt Sophia had chosen it as part of her trousseau and Alida had several more like it.

''Goodbye, Aunt Lucie,'' she was saying a few moments later as her aunt accompanied them to the door.

''Goodbye, my dear.'' Aunt Lucie smiled and added in her soft-toned attractive voice, ''You look almost scared, child. Is it Marcelle? She's a little disconcerting when you first meet her, but I'm sure you'll be good friends before very long.''

Good friends.... Alida was frowning to herself as she sat beside her mother in the car. She wanted more than anything to be friends with all her relatives...but Marcelle...? Alida was not at all sure she would be able to get on with Marcelle, let alone become her friend.

As they arrived back at her mother's home they saw a car in the drive. It was Roger's and he was standing by the edge of the lawn, watching a Red Admiral butterfly flitting about among the flowers in one of the borders. He turned with a smile, his grey eyes looking Alida over with undisguised admiration.

''Had a nice time?'' he asked. Margaret had told him, over the telephone, that they were visiting her sister.

''Yes, thank you, Roger.''

''She met Marcelle,'' put in Margaret with a grimace.

Roger stepped between them and put an arm around each as they began to walk towards the front door of the house.

"And what did you think of her?" he wanted to know, slanting Alida a glance.

"Well—er—I didn't have much time to—to form an opinion."

Roger laughed.

"Enough said! Marcelle's difficult to understand. I'd call her bitchy if it wasn't for offending your mother."

"Hmm! Much you care about offending me, or anyone else for that matter," retorted his fiancée. "I couldn't count the number of times you've called my niece bitchy."

They entered the hall and then the living-room. As always Alida experienced a little thrill of pleasure on coming into the delightful room. It was so cosy, with its wall-to-wall carpeting, its long velvet drapes of rich crimson, its antique furniture. In her father's villa there was no carpet, just tiled floors, and as the windows all had shutters because of the sun no one bothered too much about elegant curtains, just a few yards of gathered net or perhaps short drapes of flowered cotton.

"She's a nasty piece of work," Roger was saying in a belated response to Margaret's feigned indignation. "The only one of the family whom I dislike. David's a little aloof but he's genuine for all that, but Marcelle. . . ." He tailed off, frowning slightly. "An unprofitable subject," he added after a pause. "Margaret, I think I shall come with you this evening after all."

"You will?" His fiancée's eyes lighted up. "You said you had some business to attend to."

He nodded.

"I know, but it can wait. I feel like relaxing for a while before I go back to America."

"I'm glad you're coming with us," smiled Alida.

"You'll be able to book a seat for the show?" she added as the thought occurred to her.

"I've already done so," he replied casually. "I cancelled the two already booked and booked three in the dress circle."

"That'll be lovely!"

"Margaret," said Roger slowly as his appreciative eyes wandered over Alida's figure and then settled on her face, "have I told you how lucky you are to have found this enchanting child?"

"Of course—several times."

Alida coloured. She looked very beautiful, leaning back against the cushions of the sofa, with her soft brown eyes wide and innocent despite that shattering experience of a night with the Greek who was her husband, and her hair spreading like a cloak about her shoulders.

"I th-think I'll go to my room," she said, glancing from one to the other and feeling that they might like to be alone for a while. In any case, she felt a trifle unwell, having a headache and a sickly feeling in the pit of her stomach.

"All right, love," returned her mother. "Have a little rest; we'll be very late tonight."

"Yes, I will. I'll have a lie-down."

"Do that, darling." Margaret frowned slightly as she studied her face. "You're a little pale. Are you feeling all right?"

"Of course," smiled Alida reassuringly. "I'm just tired, that's all. Father always said I went pale if I was tired."

CHAPTER THREE

IT was just a week later when Alida's mind flashed the idea to her consciousness. She was having a bath, and a sort of nausea came over her. She felt light-headed and got out of the bath quickly, her heart sinking to the very depths. In the excitement of the past few weeks she had not even thought that she might be having a baby...but now.... There was very little doubt in her mind, and it was not physical sickness that affected her but the heart-sickness of despair. To be like this when she had such a wonderful future before her! It would all be spoiled. And it wasn't as if she wanted the baby—no, just the reverse! When she did eventually have a child, she had thought, she would have one with an English father.

She reached for a towel from the heated rail and wrapped it around her. What would her mother have to say? She was young and gay and liked to run around visiting, shopping, dining out and going to shows. She would not want to be hampered with a baby in the house.

Tears welled up in Alida's eyes. In her heart there was such a bitter hatred of her husband that she could almost have wished he were dead. To have done this to her.... But that was the reason for his marrying her, to produce the son that would make his father happy.

It was an effort to dry herself; she wanted to run to her mother and weep on her breast. Yet, paradoxically, she wished she could keep this from her, at least for a time. Perhaps she could—if she wasn't sick or didn't faint.

She dried herself at last, mechanically wiping her tears away with the towel. It seemed incredible that her spirits had been so light only a few hours ago. Last evening she and her mother had had a visit from her cousin David, and he and Alida had taken to one another on the instant. Tall and attractive and looking rather more than his twenty-five years, he seemed the embodiment of all that Alida had imagined an Englishman should be. His fair hair and blue eyes met instantly with her approval, perhaps, she thought, because all the men she had known had been very dark, like her husband. David's features were lean and strong, his figure slender and perfectly formed. She had been shy when he remarked on her appearance, admiring her looks and her hair and, lastly, the dress she wore, which was a new one bought by her mother at one of the fashionable shops in Southport, where they had gone the day before, to visit a friend of Margaret's who had retired there. Before leaving at well after midnight David had promised to be at the party and he would bring several of his friends, he said.

"You've made a hit," Margaret had asserted. "Marcelle will be furious."

"Does she like him, then?"

"More than likes him. He's the reason she doesn't find anyone else. She hopes that one day he'll wake up to the fact that she's beautiful. Funny thing, though, he's not dark—just tall and handsome, so he isn't really her ideal."

"I hope she doesn't think that I—that I—" Alida broke off, not knowing exactly what she wanted to say.

Her mother looked perceptively at her and remarked quietly,

"If he likes you, my love, then she'll have to accept it. There isn't anything else she can do, is there?"

Did David like her? wondered Alida. She felt she could easily come to like him... could fall in love with him....

Her mother was already in the breakfast room when she came down. She managed to smile in her customary spontaneous way as she took her place at the table.

"We're going to Manchester today, love," said Margaret. "You must have something quite special for your party."

"A long dress, you mean?"

"Yes. I'd like to see you in green—lime green. You've nothing in that colour. I hope you're not superstitious, child?"

"No, but Aunt Sophia was."

"Silly woman! I remember her; she was so plain that it was impossible for her ever to get a husband, even though she did have a substantial dowry."

"She always said she didn't want to marry."

"Every Greek girl wants to marry."

"I didn't," said Alida reflectively. "Father was horrid to force me," she added, thinking of her condition and desperately hoping that she might be mistaken.

"He always was domineering. I could never have stuck it with him—" Distress entered her mother's eyes as she looked at her daughter across the table. "I ought to have taken you with me, though, but at the time I wanted the freedom I'd been so foolish as to give up. I'd been carried away by the romance of the island, by Marcos's good looks, by the idea of marrying a foreigner. But I soon regretted the day I ever thought of choosing

Cyprus for a holiday. I'd have given ten years of my life to have gone back—'' She shrugged and, picking up the toast-rack, held it out to Alida. "One can never go back, so one must abide by one's mistakes. However, in your case it was different; you were coerced, in the manner that most Greek girls are coerced. Thank God *you've* no child on your hands! That would have been a calamity and no mistake!" She replaced the rack after Alida had taken a piece of toast, failing to notice that her hand was shaking as she picked up her knife to butter it. A calamity.... Alida felt impelled to learn more about her mother's attitude and she said, trying to sound casual,

"You wouldn't have wanted me if I'd had a child?"

The older woman frowned and said nothing for a moment. She was thoughtful, and the knife with which she had been cutting her ham was idle in her hand.

"I would certainly not have been delighted with having a baby in my house," she was honest enough to admit at last.

"It—would be a nuisance to you?" Alida cut her toast and took a bite, her soft eyes fixed upon her mother's face. She saw a hardness for the first time, both in the blue eyes and in the tightness of Margaret's mouth.

"Yes, it would, Alida. Who wants a baby around at my age? I never really know why girls want babies any more. They've no need to have them, so why they don't all take advantage of what the scientists have done for us I don't know. I shall certainly make sure I don't have any howling brats around me, even though Roger would be able to engage a nanny for them."

"If no one had babies the world would end in less than a hundred years' time."

"It wouldn't end; it would revert to the realm of the animals—and animals can take better care of the world than man ever could."

Alida looked at her curiously.

"You have very strange ideas, Mother," she said.

"You've only to look around to see what a mess man has made. Skyscrapers where there were once grassy plains; factories where there were once lovely forests of trees. Even rivers are culverted and lakes filled in."

Alida ate her toast. She reverted after a moment to the question of a child.

"I could very easily have had a child," she said.

"If you'd stayed, yes. But you had the sense to run off immediately. What a blessing it was that those people pinned money on to your dress! I hate to think what might have happened if you hadn't escaped when you did. You'd have had a baby every year. Some Greek women do."

"Not so much now," corrected Alida. "Many families are limited to three or four children."

"Well, three or four would be purgatory to me," declared her mother. "As I said, one would be a nuisance to me."

All the way to Manchester in the car Alida was going over her mother's words. Supposing she did not want her when she knew the truth? All Alida could see was a return to her husband. No! She would never return to that sort of slavery! Besides, how would Darius treat her now? His anger was something upon which Alida had refused to dwell since coming to her mother. She had successfully managed to cast her husband right out of her mind...until this morning.... One could scarcely cast the father of one's child out of one's mind.

The dress was not green after all but white, almost like a wedding-dress, thought Alida, amazed to find her memories bringing back the picture of the church and the ceremony, the banquet and the dancing. And then the night, when her husband had treated her with no more respect than he would have treated one of his pillow-friends.

"You look ravishing!" Margaret had come into her daughter's room and was standing in the doorway surveying her with both satisfaction and pride. "My, but I'm glad to have you, love! You and I are going to have some fun in the next year or two—before I get married to Roger. Then we'll all live in the States, and you might marry an American."

Alida was thinking of David, who would be at the dinner-dance tonight. David who did not know she was married and having a divorce... did not know she was having a baby....

I might not be! she thought fiercely. *No, it might all be a false alarm!*

The dinner was superb, and when it was over they went to the ballroom. Alida was claimed at once by David, who brought his cheek so close to hers that it was almost touching.

"You're beautiful, Alida," he whispered, thrilling her with his gentleness, the way he held her and the way he swung her from other dancers who might have knocked into her. She caught sight of Marcelle and a little gasp of disbelief left her lips. The girl's blue eyes were glacial, and venomous with hate. Shuddering, Alida turned her head, her heart beating far too quickly. She was glad when the dance was over and she was back with her mother and Roger. Aunt Lucie and her husband were at the bar. Joan and Mary were talking to two young men, friends of David who, Alida noticed, was walking over to join them.

And then she saw him! Her heart turned a somersault and instinctively she clutched at her mother's arm.

"Child, what—?"

"Darius, Mother! It's—it's m-my husband—" She pointed. He had entered and was standing looking all around, his very pose exuding arrogance and superiority. So tall! He towered above everyone as, not noticing his cowering wife, he began to walk across the dance floor, passing couples and groups who were chatting together.

The blood pounded in Alida's head; she was conscious of the sound of the instrumentalists tuning up, preparing to play the next dance tune; she was aware of heads turning as Darius strode forth. Who was this tall, foreign stranger? the glances seemed to be saying.

"Your husband?" from Margaret incredulously. "Here?"

"This m-man c-coming towards us," quavered Alida, her voice shaking with fear. "Oh, he's seen me! Why didn't I run?"

"Because there wasn't any need," said her mother grimly. "You're quite safe with me, child. I'll deal with him."

Roger, who had been talking to an acquaintance who had come and sat down next to him, turned swiftly as his fiancée's words caught his ear.

"What's wrong—" He got no further. Darius, having espied his wife a few seconds ago, was now standing before her, his black eyes burning like live coals. Alida shivered and edged closer to her mother. Roger stood up, looking aggressive. It was plain that he had taken in the situation.

Darius's voice seemed to come to his wife from a long way off.

"So I find you—" The music started up; he took her hand and before anyone could do anything she was jerked to her feet. "My dance, I think," said Darius in a very soft voice. "If you don't want me to make a scene, Alida, then just behave naturally. We have a great deal to discuss."

"We—we h-have nothing to discuss." A tumult of fear rose in her breast as he bore her farther and farther away from her mother. She twisted her head, saw that she and Roger were talking excitedly, but as neither made a move she realised that they had no wish to draw attention either to themselves or to the couple on the floor. There were stares, however, curious stares as the foreign-looking man, so tall and handsome, danced with his wife. Alida was suddenly conscious of Marcelle again, and of the narrowed eyes and thoughtful expression. Darius swung her away and she lost sight of the girl.

"Please t-take m-me back," faltered Alida, scarcely able to articulate words. She supposed she should have thought of the possibility of her husband searching for her, of his perhaps being told by her father that she would in all probability be with her mother in England. "I don't want you, Darius. I d-don't l-love y-you."

"We have to talk," he said but with a frown. "There isn't anywhere here where we could be private. I shall speak with you later—"

"Later?" she broke in. Her knees were trembling, like jelly. She felt faint and wanted only to sit down.

"I shall come to your mother's home—yes, I know where you are living." He looked down into her white face and added harshly, "Did you suppose for one moment that I would just forget you? Did you think that I'd suffer the humiliation of my friends knowing my wife had deserted me? You should have known better, Alida! It was no spineless Englishman you married!"

"They're not spineless!" she retorted, anger erasing her fear for a moment. "You don't know what they are like, because you've never been in England—you've never been out of Cyprus, but if you had you'd have learned that all girls are not slaves, that there's equality in the world, that we are treated with respect, and—and love!"

He stared down at her, his brow puckered a little, but rather in puzzlement than anger. It was true, he had never been out of Cyprus, true that he had been reared in a man's world where the female was regarded as vastly inferior, a vassal whose husband was the supreme master.

"I want us to talk," was all he said, but now his tone was less hard, his manner a little more conciliatory.

"It isn't any use," she said. "I'm having a divorce—"

"No. You are not!"

"My mother will see that I'm freed—" She stopped and gave a little gasp of pain as his grip tightened savagely on her hand.

"You're my wife, and that's your destiny. In Cyprus we don't allow our womenfolk to dictate to us!"

"Divorce is easy, Darius, you know that."

"In Cyprus? Yes, I agree, but it's easy only when the divorce is by mutual consent. I shall never consent to a divorce—never!"

They had reached the edge of the floor and he swung her off, and away to a vacant table under an arch hung with flowers.

"You have no choice." Alida's voice was steadier

now, and some of the colour had returned to her face. "We're in England, my mother's country—a civilised country, Darius. Oh, I love Cyprus, and never really wanted to leave it permanently, though I've always wanted to see England. But through my father forcing me into marriage I had to leave." She looked at him and her beautiful eyes were sad. "I'm sorry for the humiliation you mention," she went on in her gentle childish voice. "You shouldn't have offered for me, knowing I was half English, and that I would be almost sure to resent an arranged marriage."

He was frowning heavily; she wondered if her quiet sincerity had impressed him, because the black eyes had softened slightly and his mouth was a little less thin.

"If only you were having my child...." He seemed to be speaking to himself, and as he was not looking at her he did not notice the little start she gave or the scared expression that leapt into her eyes. He would have to know some time—Alida cut her thoughts abruptly. She was not *sure* yet! She prayed that it would prove to be a false alarm, prayed in desperation to Apostolos Andreas, the saint who looked after mothers and children. Perhaps he would not answer her prayer, on account of her not wanting the baby, but on the other hand he might feel sorry for her and be kind. "Yes, if you were having my child then you'd not be taking this attitude."

She swallowed saliva that had collected on her tongue, and then found herself saying, in a voice that sounded nothing like her own,

"Well, I'm not having your child, so you have no claim on me whatsoever—"

"Yes, I do have a claim!" His mouth twisted and his eyes glinted; he looked like Satan himself, thought

Alida with a shiver. "I shall not let you go so easily!"
His eyes were wandering over the room. "That was your
mother, I presume?—the one I saw you with when I
came in?"

"Yes."

"And the man?" His gaze was fixed upon the couple
who were standing close together, watching Alida and
her husband but making no move to join them. The
music was slow and dreamy, the tune *Ramona*, a waltz.
David, Alida noticed, was dancing with Marcelle, and
Marcelle was smiling as if she were happy and content to
be with him.

"That's Roger, Mother's fiancé," answered Alida.
"He's an American."

"Did it take you long to find your mother?"

"It was very quick, in fact."

"Pity," he said between his teeth. "Had it taken
more time you'd have had to contact me." His dark
eyes raked her with faint contempt. "How much did
you get from those damned people who decided to pin
money on your dress?"

"Five hundred pounds. It would have lasted until I
got a job."

His face twisted at the mention of a job. And his
voice was a snarl as he said.

"My wife doesn't take jobs! She wasn't meant for
menial work!"

"I'd have pleased myself." Every moment she was
gaining confidence, becoming braver. "I had no intention of returning to you, even if I hadn't found my
mother. I'd have sooner worked in someone's kitchen
than gone back to you."

He seemed staggered by her quietly-spoken statement
and for a moment seemed deprived of speech.

"You hate me as much as that?" he said at last.

She looked into his dark, aquiline face and sighed.

"I don't exactly hate you," she replied, but a trifle doubtfully as she continued to look at him. "I resented your offering for me—and—and that n-night...." She tailed off and coloured as memory flooded in. Darius opened his mouth to speak and then closed it again, waiting for his wife to continue. "You—c-could h-have been patient with m-me...." Again her accents faltered and again her husband waited, his eyes intently fixed upon her. "You were a stranger to me, Darius," she went on, still with difficulty. "It's the most terrible thing to be m-made l-love to by a stranger—and in *that* sort of way." She withdrew her gaze from his face and fell to a contemplation of her small white hands, clasped together in her lap. "If you had waited a little while, then perhaps we m-might have become friends—" She broke off and shook her head. "I think it would never have worked, Darius. As I said, I resented your offering for me. What right had you to want me for your wife?"

"The right that every Cypriot has, and every Greek! I wanted *you*, no one else, and so the right was mine to offer for you."

"Custom!" she retorted. "You followed custom!"

"What else would I follow?" he demanded roughly. "Of course I followed custom."

She lifted her eyes again and stared into his.

"That custom is becoming outdated," she asserted, and now her voice was gentle again, and less hostile. "I'm not a Cypriot girl and therefore I should not have been subjected to a custom I didn't approve of."

It was her husband's turn to sigh.

"I suppose I should have thought a little more about your parentage," he admitted surprisingly. "However, you are married to me, Alida, and you'll have to abide by it.''

Her gaze was straight and challenging.

"Do you really believe you can force me to return to you?''

"Don't you love the island you were brought up in?'' He regarded her with censure. "Don't you miss Cyprus?''

"Certainly I do,'' she was ready to own, thinking nostalgically of the pale beaches and the vivid blue sea, the sweet-smelling oleanders that lined the dry stream bed running through her father's garden, the scent of the freesias growing wild in the hillside hollows, the orange groves and lemon groves, where the fruit resembled little Chinese lanterns nestling amid glossy green foliage. The mountains and valleys, the unhurried bustle of Nicosia. Oh, yes, she missed her beautiful island and knew for sure that she would return one day—perhaps not to stay, but certainly for a visit.

"Well then, why aren't you willing to come back with me?''

She wondered if he had realised it—that he had virtually admitted that he could not force her to return with him to the island.

"Because, as I said, I don't love you.''

"Love!'' he ejaculated contemptuously. "Women's stuff! I have already said it!''

His wife's brown eyes were misted all at once. How very sad that he and all those others in lands like Cyprus would never know what love was.

"Perhaps it's women's stuff in your country, Darius, but here, where I belong now, men fall in love too.'' Where I belong.... She still felt like an alien sometimes, she thought, and hoped she would eventually come to regard England as her homeland.

"You do not belong here!" flashed Darius harshly. "Cyprus is your country, as it is mine! You'll soon sicken of this climate, and the hurry and bustle of the people here! In Cyprus we have time for other things than making money!"

"So do they here have time for other things."

"Such as?"

Her eyes met his again.

"Falling in love," she replied simply, and her glance just happened to stray to David, who caught it as he danced and gave her a swift smile. She responded, and for a few seconds her eyes shone. Marcelle had her back to Alida and so missed this rather affectionate exchange. But Darius did not miss it, and his teeth actually gritted together.

"Who the devil's that?" he demanded, embers of fury darkening his pagan eyes.

"A friend, Darius."

"Married women do not have men friends!" he told her savagely, half rising as though he intended approaching David and making a scene. Alida's breath caught and a quivering spasm of apprehension affected her heart. If Darius should go over to David, and say he was her husband....

"He isn't that sort of friend," she said hastily, relieved to see him settle in his chair again.

He glowered at her.

"*What* sort of a friend?" he almost snarled. "Answer me!"

She coloured, and was aware of her mother looking at her. She felt instinctively that she would be over in a moment or two, being unable any longer to stand by and await the result of this conversation between her daughter and her husband. Roger was by her side, quite ready to lend his support to any move his fiancée might decide to make. The presence of those two had sustained Alida during these past few minutes, but she had no wish that they should give Darius any excuse for making a scene at her party, the party she was enjoying despite the heaviness of the doubts regarding her condition.

"He's a cousin, really," she faltered, her eyes falling beneath the wild fury of her husband's concentrated gaze. "I've four cousins and two aunts and an uncle."

"How nice," with sarcasm and the hint of a sneer. "Plenty of support, eh? I suppose they are all here tonight?"

"Yes, they are."

"And all ready to stick up for you against your husband?"

"They don't know—" Too late she stopped, her scared eyes meeting his incredulous ones.

"They don't know you're married?" The words came slowly, in a voice edged with disbelief. "Whose idea was that?"

"My mother decided that as long as I was going to be divorced, it was not necessary—at least for the present—to tell anyone I was married."

"Your mother, eh?" he said grittingly. "Very concerned for you all at once! Have you forgotten that she deserted you when you were a baby?"

"I haven't forgotten," replied Alida quietly, "but I've forgiven her. I think she was most unhappy with my father."

"Is that an excuse for leaving her child? If we'd had a child would you have deserted it?"

She shook her head automatically and her heart grew tender.

"No... I could never leave my child, but people are made differently, Darius, and we have to be tolerant." So gentle her voice, so deeply understanding the look in her eyes. Darius, appearing to be touched in some indefinable way, said to her,

"You weren't tolerant with me, though."

"That was different. You hurt me, treating me without respect—" She spread her hands in a little helpless gesture. "It isn't important any more, Darius," she said. "We weren't suited, so we shall have a divorce. We shall both one day find the one to suit us."

"I never shall!" he returned, hardening again. "I'm married to you and I intend to stay that way! Do you suppose I shall give you up without a struggle? I shall fight, Alida, and I shall win!"

"It's impossible," she assured him. "There's no doubt at all that I can get my freedom. In fact, Mother's considering the possibility of an annulment, seeing that I was coerced into marriage against my will!"

"It wasn't against your will! You weren't bound and gagged when you entered the church!"

She gave a deep sigh and shook her head. She was anxious to bring this conversation to an end.

"You know very well what I mean, Darius." Her soft brown eyes were wide and appealing as they stared into his. "Leave me alone," she begged. "You can't gain anything by causing me trouble. I've had enough—the running away, for one thing. It wasn't easy, you know. I was very scared and didn't know if I would find my mother or not. I landed in a strange country, all on my own, and I'd never been anywhere before. So please be kind and leave me alone."

His arrested expression seemed at first to be an assurance that her plea had gone home, for his eyes were softer than she had ever seen them and even the silence was soothing, devoid of hostility or rancour. But even as she watched his face changed; his eyes became hard and unyielding.

"I shall fight you!" he declared, his tone harsh and bitter. "You married me willingly and by God, you'll abide by it!"

She saw her mother coming towards them, drawn by the conviction that Alida was in need now of her support. Alida suspected she had told Roger to stay behind, because he had made no attempt to follow her.

"So you are Darius?" said Margaret without preamble, and took the chair he offered. Reaching over, he picked up another and sat down again.

"Yes, it's Darius." It was Alida who spoke, for the other two were subjecting one another to an intensive stare. Margaret frowned as the silence stretched; she told her daughter afterwards that Darius's cold and merciless face gave her the shivers. But it was a handsome face, she had to admit, an arresting face which was marred only by the pagan quality of the features. It was no wonder she had run from him, Margaret added.

"Why," she said breaking the silence at last, "have you come here?"

His narrowed eyes bored right into her.

"To collect my wife," he snapped.

"Indeed?" Margaret asked haughtily and with a lift of her exquisitely fashioned eyebrows. "And what makes you suppose that you can take my daughter from me?"

"She's my wife!"

"By coercion," returned Margaret blandly. She was as cool as it was possible to be. Alida wished she had half her confidence and poised assurance. "You would be wise to forget that Alida was ever your wife, Mr. Valaris. It was silly of you to come here thinking you could drag her away." She looked at him and added, "What arrogance you Greeks possess! Marcos was just the same. He always said I'd belong to him for life."

Alida shivered as she saw her husband's expression change. He looked ready to murder her mother—no, ready to torture her, slowly, relentlessly.

"I have certain rights, madam," he snapped, "and I shall fight to retain them!"

"Fight away," she scoffed. "Much good will it do you!"

A small silence and then,

"I believe that you've passed my wife off as a single woman?"

For the first time Margaret was put out of countenance.

"You told him?" She frowned at her daughter. "There was no need, surely?"

"I could stand up, this minute, and declare myself to be her husband." He glanced around as he spoke, a significant gesture that was not lost on Margaret or her daughter."

"Please don't," begged Alida before her mother could speak. "What good would it do you?"

"It would at least keep other men away!" he snarled.

"Alida's not interested in other men," from Margaret swiftly. "All she wants is peace, and to see something of life. She's far too young to settle down to married life—especially married life such as she would have had with you. And with you, there'd be slavery into the bargain! No, my man, you are never getting Alida into those clutches of yours again, so you can go away and resign yourself to accepting the divorce!''

CHAPTER FOUR

THE uncertainty was at an end. Alida at last admitted resignedly that she was expecting her husband's child. She sat on the edge of the bed in her beautiful room and wept bitter tears, for the future looked bleak indeed. Her mother would not want the child, and Alida did not blame her. As she had said, she had no wish to have a baby in the house at this time in her life. Margaret was having a good time at present. Roger was, she admitted, a lucky find, as he was rich and good-looking and he had fallen in love with her on sight. Margaret loved him, but, as she had told Alida, she did not want to get married for a while yet.

For some weeks after her admission Alida pondered on what was the wisest course to take. She could return to her husband, but that would be her very last resort. She wished she were older, had more knowledge of the world, had more idea of how to cope with a situation like this. She knew that other girls must have been faced with the same problem, and they had managed to cope. But she had been sheltered all her life, living in a small village surrounded by people who were all related to her father, people who would have reported it at once if she had put a foot wrong. True, she had been allowed to go to school in Nicosia, but it had not equipped her to deal with this kind of crisis.

As the weeks went by she was becoming more and

more afraid, and yet she kept her secret to herself. Her mother said one day, her eyes sweeping Alida's figure,

"You're filling out, my love. The new life agrees with you, obviously. But don't put on too much weight; keep your figure—it's a very lovely one."

Alida had been more afraid than ever then, shocked into the knowledge that she could not remain silent very much longer.

Her social life was designed by her mother to make up in some measure for the years she had been restricted by her father. Margaret took her out dancing, to shows, to concerts in Manchester and Liverpool. Roger had suggested they have a holiday at his beautiful mansion in Miami Beach, and normally Alida would have been thrilled with the idea, but in her present state of mind she had no enthusiasm for going abroad.

"We're invited to Marcelle's twenty-first birthday party," Margaret informed Alida one day. "It's to be held in the Concert Hall in Baybridge—that's not far from Chester, you know."

The mention of a party naturally put Alida in mind of her own, and the unexpected appearance of her husband. He had not given up hope of forcing her to return to him, and as Roger declared, his arrogance and pompous attitude were almost unbelievable. He came to Margaret's house the following day and demanded to see his wife. Roger ordered him off the doorstep, but he refused to go and, taking Roger unawares, thrust past him and walked into the room where Alida was standing, every nerve tensed, her pulses racing and her heart seeming to have come right up and settled in her throat. Her mother was not in and Darius strode across the room, seizing his wife cruelly by the wrist. She thought: how like the Greek male he is! With that superior dominating manner, that undue assumption of superiority.

"You!" he spat. "Get your coat on; you're coming with me!"

But Roger was there and to Alida's horror the men began to fight. She shrank into a corner as furniture and ornaments went flying, wishing she could get past the men and into the hall where the telephone was. Roger was a powerful man, but Darius had the advantage of youth and in the end Alida was driven to seeking something with which to hit her husband. She was just picking up a long-handled brass poker when her mother appeared in the doorway.

"Don't!" she warned, looking at her daughter. "I'll phone for the police!"

She had taken in the situation at once and wisely prevented Alida from an action which might have resulted in something that she could have had on her mind for the rest of her life. The two men stopped their battle as Margaret's words penetrated. Darius, glowering at her, and with perspiration pouring from his face, snarled the words,

"Get the police! If they know what they're about they'll tell me to take my wife home and give her a beating!"

"That," quavered Alida, "is what might happen in Cyprus—"

"But not here!" broke in Margaret, glancing at her fiancé and seeing the cut on his lip. "Your Cyprus police might consider your sex as masters, but here, let me tell you, we're more enlightened!" She glanced at Alida and her mouth compressed. "How dare you come here putting fear into my child! If I have my way you'll spend the night in jail!"

Darius, accepting defeat, left before the police arrived, although he did stand there while Margaret phoned, a sneer twisting his lips into sheer ugliness. Alida, standing by the sitting-room door, had shivered visibly, and had felt the comfort of Roger's arm as it came about her shoulders.

"My God," said Margaret when Darius had eventually made his departure, "it's lucky for you that you managed to get away from that fiend! I had an angel in comparison!"

"You poor child," murmured Roger, and it was plain that he was imagining Alida's terror when she found herself at her husband's mercy, after a wedding she had never wanted. "That man has a lot to learn."

"Well, he might learn—but he'll never get my daughter back!"

Margaret had insisted that Alida go up to her room and rest, but the upset had so unnerved her that she was violently ill for several minutes. And she had felt faint again, and despair enveloped her as a result.

The next time she had seen Marcelle the older girl had asked curiously,

"Who was the tall dark foreigner you were dancing with at the party?"

"Oh," returned Alida casually, "just an acquaintance from Cyprus. He's here on holiday—"

"And so we invited him to Alida's party, naturally." The smooth, deliberate interruption had come from Margaret, who had very conveniently come upon the two girls and so relieved her daughter of the necessity of any further questioning from her cousin. But Marcelle was plainly intrigued, and on another occasion had questioned Alida about the stranger. This time Alida changed the subject abruptly, and made her escape, having been forewarned by her mother and told what to do. Margaret and Roger were worried that Darius would cause more trouble, would find some of the relatives and tell them that he was her husband.

"I hope it isn't Marcelle he gets into contact with," said Roger. "She'll probe and probe until she has the whole story."

"Well, so what if she does?" Margaret wanted to know. "What good will it do her?"

However, they need not have worried, because Darius just disappeared and they had heard nothing of him again.

"Darling, you're a thousand miles away!" Margaret laughed softly as she uttered the words. Alida looked at her and laughed deprecatingly.

"I was thinking about *my* party, and the way Darius turned up."

A sudden frown was her mother's only reaction for a space as she too mentally brought back that particular occasion.

"Forget him, love. You'll soon be free of him altogether."

"He'll fight a divorce."

"Let him! When he finds himself defeated he'll begin to realise that he's not the Almighty!"

Yes, mused Alida, the experience of being defeated would certainly be a chastening one for a man who believed that men were the masters and women their vassals.

Marcelle looked superb in a gown of emerald green satin, sleek in style and in fit, accentuating her seductive curves. But she seemed insignificant beside her cousin, even though Alida was dressed simply in a long dress of sapphire blue organza, high-throated and with sleeves gathered into tight cuffs to which were attached small ribbon bows, matching those down the front of the bodice. Margaret had chosen it, and her taste was always excellent. She had a flair for clothes, just as she had a flair for hair-styles and for finding the correct pieces of jewellery to wear for any set occasion. Alida merely wore a small diamond in her hair, a gift to her mother from Roger—one of the many beautiful pieces that he had lavished on her from time to time.

The party was a buffet, which was laid out in a large room off the main dance floor, and as soon as Alida arrived with her mother and Roger she was claimed by David who said he was not only having every dance with her but was taking her to supper as well. Overhearing this, Marcelle scowled and turned away, but not for long was she able to ignore the girl of whom she was jealous, the girl who had come into the family circle and captured all the limelight. For undoubtedly Alida was lovely, and her new-found relatives never spared her blushes when, as on an occasion such as this, they felt the urge to compliment her on her appearance. Margaret scorned her niece's attitude while Roger maintained that the girl would actually do Alida an injury if she could.

"Joan and Mary are so different," he had gone on to say, referring to Alida's other cousins. "They seem delighted at having another member added to the family."

"It so happens that they aren't after David, though," Margaret pointed out. "Marcelle's always hoped she'd get somewhere with David, but now she has competition and it's brought out everything that's nasty in her."

"Nasty?" repeated Roger with a lift of his brows. "Once again you're being generous towards the girl. I'd say she was downright malicious towards Alida, and of course, as you imply, jealousy's the cause.''

Alida had overheard this interchange and she had thought bitterly that her cousin had no need to be jealous; she was quite safe, because she, Alida, was not only married but was expecting a child. Marcelle would soon know that she had nothing to fear from Alida, and so would David soon know that the girl he was beginning to like was not for him. Perhaps he would then turn to Marcelle, and Alida could not help feeling a slight pang of jealousy herself because there was no doubt in her mind that, had she been free, she could have reciprocated any encouragement David might have given her. She sighed for what might have been, and wondered bleakly what was to become of her and whether in the end she would be driven to returning to her husband.

Marcelle came up to Alida and David when eventually they went in to supper. She picked up a plate and walked alongside them, going the length of the overloaded buffet table and picking up some delicacy now and then.

''Don't eat too much,'' she whispered in Alida's ear. ''You're putting on weight—fast. Must be the change in your diet.''

Alida, taken my surprise, let her plate tilt so that the chicken roll she had taken fell to the floor. And at the same time her colour had risen because of Marcelle's remark and because David had turned and was looking her over.

''I—I . . .'' She glanced down, but it was David who stooped to take up the roll and put it to one side. ''Thank you,'' murmured Alida, acutely conscious that her blush, and her action, had caught and held the interest of the girl who had caused it all.

"Did I embarrass you by remarking on your altered figure?" An amused sneer accompanied the malicious words, words that were whispered, since Marcelle had no wish that they should be overheard by David who would find them not only spiteful but downright rude.

"I don't think my figure's changed that much." Alida had no idea how she managed to get the words out; she did know that her blush was deepening all the time, and that she had automatically turned to one side so that she was facing David and had her back to the other girl. But she had turned only after Marcelle had noticed the deepening of her colour, and Alida heard a long-drawn breath and in a panic-stricken moment of fear she felt sure that her cousin had guessed the truth. But soon Alida was chiding herself for her anxiety. Marcelle could not possibly have guessed at her condition. Had she known she was married it would have been different, but as it was she believed her cousin to be single.

"Shall we sit here?" David turned to Alida who had followed him to a table.

"Yes—".

"You've nothing on your plate!" he exclaimed, glancing at it. "Aren't you hungry?"

She began to say yes, she was, but suddenly realised that she had never felt less like eating. She stared at her empty plate and wished she were somewhere else, wished she were alone, alone with her misery and her fears and her picture of a future that seemed black from start to finish.

"May I sit with you?" from Marcelle in a tone of smooth velvet. "I'm sorry you're not eating," she added with a smile as she turned to her cousin, whose face was pallid now, and her young mouth quivering.

"Do have something," urged David, putting down

his plate and turning to her. "What can I get you?" His voice was gentle, and edged with concern. "Perhaps you'd enjoy something sweet—a pastry of some kind?"

She nodded absently and her voice was husky when she spoke.

"Yes, please, David—one of those Danish pastries will do."

He went off with her empty plate and Marcelle turned to her immediately.

"Aunt Margaret never did say why you left Cyprus, and your father—oh, I recall that she said something about his wanting to force you into marriage, so you decided to come to England, but none of us really took that in—"

"You didn't? Why?" The question leapt to Alida's lips and could not be stemmed. But once voiced it was regretted. It should not have been said; it had a ring of guilt about it—and fear.

Marcelle's eyes narrowed to mere slits.

"It wasn't the reason, was it, Alida!" Soft the tone now, and coming from the back of Marcelle's throat—like the soft guttural sound that a jungle beast utters on sighting its prey.

"Yes," faltered Alida, "it—it was the r-reason. . . ." Why was she so lacking in confidence? she wondered, then admitted that she could scarcely be anything else but lacking in confidence, living the sheltered existence she had up till coming to England. School in Nicosia had given her a little self-confidence, but that had soon disappeared once she had left and resumed the boring existence to which her over-cautious father had condemned her.

David returned promptly, and so Marcelle had no further opportunity of questioning her cousin. But something else was to occur which was to force Alida to make her decision and tell her mother of her condition.

Alida had gone to visit her Aunt Lucie about a week after Marcelle's party. Margaret had promised to lend her sister a mink wrap, because Lucie was going to a dinner dance given by her husband's boss, and Margaret, who had an appointment at the hairdresser's asked Alida to take the wrap, which she did, going early in the afternoon so as to make sure she would not see Marcelle, who did not leave work until five. But to Alida's consternation she found her cousin at home, reclining on the couch with a glossy magazine, and Lucie was nowhere about.

"Where's Aunt Lucie?" asked Alida when after being shown into the sitting-room by the daily help, she saw Marcelle there.

"She's gone out to do some shopping." Marcelle tossed the book aside and slid from the couch. "She won't be long. I see you brought the wrap." Her eyes moved slowly from the wrap which Alida held over her arm to her face, pale and drawn, and with little lines of tiredness at the corners of her eyes.

"I'll leave it, then, and go." Alida put the wrap on to a chair. "Er—are you unwell—or something, Marcelle?"

"Have a cold," was the brief answer.

"Oh—well, you'll need to—to keep warm," stammered Alida.

"It isn't cold," sarcastically from Marcelle, and then, after a pause, "You don't look all that robust yourself," she observed softly. "It would seem that you, too, are feeling off-colour."

Alida nodded mechanically, and unlocked her fingers. They had been clenched around one another and now her palms were damp. She had a headache and she felt sick . . . very sick.

"Yes," she murmured, "so I'd better be getting home."

"Have you been seeing David this past week?" The question came right out of the blue, taking Alida completely by surprise.

"No," she replied, "I haven't seen him since the party."

"He's taken to you," observed Marcelle, and her lips went tight. "Before you came here it was me he wanted to be with!" No attempt at friendliness now; Marcelle's eyes were slits of hate as they slid over her cousin's figure.

"That's a strange thing to say," began Alida. "I mean—if he wanted you then he'd say so. . . ." Her voice trailed off to silence as she realised all too late that her lack of experience in dealing with situations such as this had resulted in her voicing words that completely lacked tact. Marcelle's lips snapped together; she was working herself into a fury and it dawned on Alida that she had probably been in the throes of jealous anger ever since the night of her birthday party. "I'm sorry," quavered Alida, moving towards the door. "I didn't think. . . . I want you to know that there can never be anything between David and me." Would that satisfy her? she wondered, her big eyes wandering over Marcelle's curvaceous body and coming to rest on her face again. "I must go. . . ." The room began to spin and she flung out a hand to find something to grasp. But she fell, sliding almost gently on to the carpet at her cousin's feet, and her last conscious thought was that she was going to be sick on her aunt's spotless carpet.

She was on the floor when she came round, her head

resting on a cushion and her cousin bending over her. She no longer experienced the terrible nausea, but instead a drowsiness enveloped her, a lethargy that was a barrier to clear thought. She could have stayed here for ever, turning her mind into a sleep that never ended. Depression, soul-dragging and pernicious, smothered her like a blanket. She knew instinctively in this moment that she was going to have to endure a great deal of pain and discomfort in the carrying of the child she did not want. Tears welled up in her eyes, but she became grimly aware of her cousin's strange, unfathomable gaze fixed upon her and it was with a sudden sense of urgency that she got herself to a sitting position.

"What a s-silly th-thing to do," she faltered, praying fervently that she was being convincing. "I must be tired."

"Probably," without an atom of expression from Marcelle. "You didn't look as if you'd had any sleep to me, when you came through that door." A small pause and then, slowly and with emphasis, "Did you have any sleep, Alida?"

"Of course," answered Alida shortly, lowering her lashes to prevent those shrewd eyes from reading the lie in hers. She had not slept properly for weeks, ever since the moment when she had admitted that she was pregnant. "I must go home." Somehow—and without any offer of help coming from Marcelle—she dragged herself to her feet, where for a few seconds she swayed precariously, her legs like jelly and an empty sensation in the pit of her stomach. Without thinking she put a trembling hand to it...and saw her cousin's eyes dart to it, then narrow and darken as the glimmer of a smile hovered on her lips.

Margaret looked at her daughter aghast.

"But why didn't you tell me before now?" she demanded furiously, her face as white as Alida's. "To wait so long— Oh, I have no patience with you at all!"

Alida started to cry; she had known she would as soon as she made her confession and witnessed her mother's reaction. Margaret, standing with her back to the wide window of the cosy sitting-room of her home, was gritting her teeth, and her slender white hands were moving convulsively at her sides.

"I'll go," whispered Alida in a tone of despair. "I shall have to go back to Darius, there's nothing else I can do. He'll gloat, and—and...." The tears came faster, but her mother, still suffering from the effects of the shock she had received, made no attempt to comfort her. "I wish I were dead," murmured Alida, but to herself. "I'm sorry for all the trouble I've caused, Mother...." Again her voice faltered to a stop. She had not mentioned the scene that had been enacted at her aunt's house, and she knew that although Marcelle would be almost sure to mention it to other members of the family, she would not dare to imply that Alida was expecting a child—no, she dared not, because Alida was not supposed to be married, and to say she was expecting a baby would, at this stage, be tantamount to slander, and Marcelle was much too wise to say anything until she was sure. And by that time everyone would be sure, because she could scarcely hide her secret for very much longer. "I'll go," she said again, lifting her tear-filled eyes and staring at her mother across the room. "I should never have come in the first place," she quavered, a sob catching every single word that left her lips, a sob that rose from the very depths of her. "I never even thought about a baby...and yet I should have done, shouldn't I?" Her mother said nothing and Alida continued by saying that she could understand her not wanting a child in her home at her time of life, and that she would not think any the less of her for letting her return to Cyprus!

"You'll not be returning to Cyprus!"

Both occupants of the room darted a glance towards the open door. Roger, more grim and stern than Alida would ever have believed possible, stood there, statue-still, and it was more than plain that he had heard almost everything that had been said in the last few minutes. He must have been in the hall, thought Alida, because he certainly had not been standing there for very long. He advanced into the room, his eyes never wavering from their fixation on his fiancée's white face.

"I'm ashamed of you," was all he said, in that quiet, refined American voice that always sounded so attractive to Alida. He came to her, and within seconds she was in his arms, her hot and bitter tears dampening his snow-white shirt. Sobs racked her and he held her close. Then her mother, appearing to have awakened from a sort of trance that had prevented her from showing pity, came across the room and opened her arms.

"I'm sorry, child," she said hoarsely. "I'd not the slightest intention of letting you go back to that monster, but, Alida, you gave me such a shock that I was practically knocked out. You see, it was natural that such a possibility had occurred to me right at the beginning, but I guess I had put it out of my mind when nothing appeared to have happened." She had come close and gently she tilted Alida's chin. "If only you'd taken precautions. . . ." Her voice trailed as she caught her fiancé's expression and she shrugged her shoulders resignedly.

Alida's face was blank and innocent.

"I wouldn't know how—" she breathed, her face reflecting the despair enveloping her heart.

"It doesn't matter now," broke in Roger gently. "We have to consider the situation as it is," he said, turning to Margaret, "not as it might have been."

"Yes, you're right, of course," agreed Margaret with a sigh. "What's the best thing? You seem to have an idea."

He nodded.

Alida looked from one to the other, her heart lighter than she would have ever imagined a few short moments ago.

"Thank you," she said simply. "Thank you both." And she moved then, saying she would like to lie down for a little while, if they didn't mind.

"No, dearest," said her mother soothingly, "of course we don't mind. In any case, I'm sure we shall be able to discuss this matter, and to see what's best for you, between ourselves."

Alida nodded her dark head.

"Yes, I think so too," she returned with the trace of a smile on her childish lips. "I'm so very grateful," she quavered. And on that she went out, feeling that she had been reprieved from a lifetime of misery and bondage.

"I wish Roger had been my father," she was thinking a few minutes later when she was undressing in her bedroom, intending to get into bed and stay there for an hour or so before getting ready for the dinner that Roger was taking them to at the Grosvenor Hotel. "Yes, he would have been a wonderful father to me. It's a shame he has no children—a shame that he never married when he was young. But perhaps he was always waiting for someone like my mother."

She got between the cool sheets and within minutes had fallen into a peaceful, dreamless slumber.

CHAPTER FIVE

TROPICAL foliage sheltering a landscaped garden, sunlight playing on clear crystal fountains, orchid trees in full bloom with bright humming-birds hovering above them. Scarlet hibiscus...lemon allamandas...purple bougainvillea.... An island in the sun....

Coral Cay in the Bahamas, one of the numerous Out Islands that lay strung like jewels on the blue Atlantic just across the Gulf Stream from the shores of Florida. The Cay was a little world of its own no more than two and a half miles long, lush and green with a sleepy lagoon whose waters lapped the talcum-soft shore and whose seaward side was protected by the lovely coral reef. Beyond the reef the waters of the Atlantic shone blue and jade and aquamarine in the sunshine, and away on the horizon a graceful white liner cruised its leisurely way towards the lovely island of New Providence.

Alida, serene and beautiful and honey-bronzed, lay relaxing in a lounger on the velvet-smooth lawn of Mangrove Lodge, one of the two fabulous homes owned by her stepfather, his other home being in the famous Miami Beach in Florida. A book was open on her lap but she was not reading, her attention having been caught and held in fascinated pleasure by a dainty woodstar, the Bahamian hummingbird whose iridescent violet throat feathers stood out, strikingly beautiful in the sunlight. It hovered above a brilliant hibiscus bloom, but even as she watched it darted away, to disappear into a clump of primrose-willows which had been left to flourish in wild profusion at one corner of the lawn.

A faint smile touched her mouth as she waited hopefully for it to come back, then her thoughts strayed for a few moments to that dark period in her life when she had carried the child she did not want. She had been in and out of the hospital, at death's door at the end....

She sighed and attempted to think of something else, but for some reason everything rose clearly before her and she seemed to be re-living what had happened in the past... eight years ago.

Her mother and Roger had decided that the best thing was for them to get married and move to Roger's home in Miami Beach, and it was here that Alida, after a great deal of suffering, had her child, a stillborn boy. And she had been in a coma for days, her life in the balance. When she did come round she was told by her mother that her baby was dead. It was strange, she reflected, that over and over again she had told her mother that she did not want the child, and yet at the end, when the real throes of agony were crucifying her, she had wanted her child, had even told herself that it would all be worthwhile when they put her baby into her arms.

Questions to her mother had gained her only vague answers, abrupt and dismissing, and Alida had guessed that Margaret was trying to spare her the pain of knowing any details about the baby. Still, she would have grasped at any crumb of information about her child—a child neither she nor Darius would ever see.

Darius.... Thoughts of him would invade her consciousness, no matter how she tried to block them out.

Strangely, she wished he could have known about their son, shared her misery and perhaps thus lighten her burden. But he hadn't known, and never would.

Alida had eventually recuperated and had become resigned to the fact that she had given birth to a stillborn child. But the mental pain had never gone away.

Her thoughts, sun-drowsed and becoming less clear, switched to the little son of her friend, Katie Gorman, whose father owned the only hotel on the Cay, the Fair Dawning. Katie's child, Roddy, was having a birthday soon, his sixth. Her own child, thought Alida, would have been in his eighth year now, had he lived.

Alida's thoughts switched even yet again, to her husband. He had defended the divorce, but Roger had secured a brilliant lawyer who gained the sympathy of the judge with his story of a forced marriage of a girl of seventeen to a man she scarcely knew. Darius wrote to say he was staggered by the absurdities of the English marriage laws and ended by stating quite firmly that he still considered he was married to Alida and he always would do so. She did not reply, following her mother's advice to make a complete break.

She had thoroughly enjoyed her life since her recovery from the crisis of the baby's birth. She and her mother often stayed on at Mangrove Lodge when Roger returned to Miami Beach. His business was in Florida, so it was necessary for him to spend a good proportion of his time there, but he got away to Coral Cay as much as he could and Alida was always happiest when he was here. She loved him dearly, more than she loved her mother. In fact, she could not love her mother to any real depth; she had no explanation for this, because her desire was to be close, to make up for those lost years of affection and companionship. However, Alida and

Margaret got along very well indeed even without deep love. They had respect for one another; they each admired the gifts possessed by the other, and they were completely happy in each other's company. Alida had wanted to get a job, but Roger would not hear of it. The only work to be had on Coral Cay was at the hotel or in one of the shops. But it would be degrading for him to have his daughter employed in such work, Roger had said, and in deference to his wishes Alida had given up the idea.

On the island she was in the swim with everything, as was her mother. The hotel provided a pleasant place to dine and dance; there were floor shows with limbo dancers and calypso bands. There were always new faces there, people on vacation, mainly from Florida but from other parts of the United States as well. Sometimes Alida would meet English people holidaying on the Cay, but not often. In any case, the island was still almost totally unspoiled and as there was nothing in the way of entertainments other than those provided by the one hotel, Coral Cay was not frequented very much at all, a circumstance that suited the people who had built themselves beautiful holiday homes here in the hope of "getting away from it all" at least for part of the year. The owners of these homes were usually American businessmen like Roger. Most of them owned magnificent yachts, which they sailed to the island, then moored the yachts in the marina to the north of the long, palm fringed beach of pink coral sand.

"Darling, are you asleep...?" Her mother's quiet voice brought Alida from her drowsy reverie and she turned, her brain fluid and alive again instantly. A smile came readily as she said no, she was not asleep, but she had been dreaming all the same. "What about, my love?'' Margaret advanced slowly, taking in the delightful picture she saw—her beautiful daughter. More beautiful now even than when she had first come to her, for there was about her an added serenity, an ethereal loveliness that had come with maturity and with the peaceful existence she was enjoying. Margaret's thoughts went momentarily to Darius and she shuddered. Thank God Alida had escaped! Where would she have been today if she had not escaped? She'd have been a prisoner, prematurely aged, and with six or seven children, probably.

"Oh, many things—" Alida swung a hand. "This little piece of Paradise for one. How did it come to be broken off, do you think?"

"Alida, you say the nicest things. But you're quite right about Coral Cay; it is a little piece that somehow got itself broken off from paradise island.''

"I only hope that no one comes here—a speculator, for instance—and spoils it by providing the sort of amenities that attract hordes of tourists.''

"It could happen,'' sighed her mother. "Look what happened to some of the other islands.''

"I suppose change does have to come. People want more comforts and so they commercialise these beautiful islands.''

Margaret made no comment, but moved to take possession of the vacant chair opposite to the one occupied by her daughter, and which had been put out earlier by one of the servants employed by Roger.

"It's better than Cyprus—you obviously think so." Margaret leant back, stretching her sun-tanned legs luxuriously. She was in a bikini, as was Alida, and her figure was still perfect.

"Yes, I think I like it better than Cyprus,'' answered Alida but not until she had thought about it. "Cyprus

was my home for so long. I loved it at one time...."
She paused reflectively. "Yes, Coral Cay is better—it's
different altogether."

"And in a different place on the map."

Alida nodded her dark head. Her hair was much
longer than she had had it after the birth of her baby; it
had been expertly cut and styled and it shone as she
moved her head, shone richly dark and faintly waved,
flicking up at the ends and with the attractive half-fringe
also flicking up, to one side of her forehead.

"The Tropics.... Sounds romantic—even the
name—doesn't it?"

Margaret nodded absently. Her eyes were on Alida's
figure and after a moment she said,

"How lovely you are, my child," and there seemed to
be a trace of regret in her voice, an impression that was
strengthened for Alida when she added, "I used to be
like you once, slim and neat and with my contours
firm."

"What a thing to say—you *used* to be like me! Why,
you look like a girl of eighteen!"

"Not eighteen," her mother laughed. "You, my
child, are almost twenty-six, and I'm sure I don't look
younger than you!"

"Twenty-six...." The words were no more than a
whisper; her youth was drifting by and she was still unmarried. Roger had often made subtle references to some
young man or other—sons of his business friends—
pointing out to Alida that they were very interested in
her, but she had not yet found herself interested. She was
happy and content and it seemed sometimes that she
would be satisfied with this life for the rest of her days.
But at other times she knew with a sort of poignant intensity a sense of loss, a lack of fulfilment in her life. This

feeling came whenever she was with Roddy, her friend's little boy, and she would wish then that her own child had lived.

She sometimes thought of his father and wondered if he were married now, with several children. For in spite of his emphatic assertion that he considered himself still married to Alida, she was sure that he had very soon realised the futility of such an attitude. Had he improved with age? He was thirty-two now, but she felt he would not have changed much at all; people never did change in any dramatic way, simply because character and personality were shaped early in one's life. Roger had once said that Darius might improve with age, she recalled, might come to realise that women were not for enslaving, admit that a wife could be a delightful friend and companion and lover.

There were times when Alida would wonder why she could not forget her former husband entirely, but then she would find herself providing the logical explanation that a girl could scarcely forget the man who had given her a child.

"Dreaming again, my love?" Margaret smiled as Alida glanced at her. "What is it this time?"

"I was thinking about Darius," she replied frankly. "And wondering what's happened to him in the past eight years."

"What an unprofitable way to spend one's time," reproved her mother. "Who cares what the wretched fellow's doing now?" She paused, then said, watching her daughter's face as if anxious to see some change of expression, "Don't you ever think about marrying? There are several charming young men, both here and in Miami, who would like to court you."

"I expect I shall meet the right one some day," responded Alida a trifle wistfully.

"What about Vance Haldene? He's head over heels in love with you—and you know it. His father's a millionaire and he's an only child, so—"

"I shall never let money influence me," interrupted Alida. "I want to marry for love, and I shall do just that, or not marry at all."

"Well, love is important," agreed Margaret without hesitation. "But if you can have love and money so much the better."

"Like you and Roger."

"Yes, like us. He was a good find, as I once said, but he considers that I was a good find too."

"You get on so well together."

"Always have done so. Roger's not very demanding and perhaps that's the secret of our success."

Alida had to smile.

"You're very honest, Mother," she said, absently taking up her book and closing it.

"About not being able to love deeply?"

Alida gave a slight start at the question; she had not expected to hear it.

"I didn't mean quite that," she began, when her mother interrupted her.

"Subconsciously you did, dear. I admit I'm not over-endowed with the ability to love as deeply as I believe you can. It's unfortunate but unremediable, a mere matter of genetics. One inherits certain traits from way back in one's ancestral line. I don't happen to have the genes for deep and abiding love." She paused a moment, but Alida said nothing and she continued, "I *can't* have the genes for deep and abiding love, can I, otherwise I'd not have been able to leave you as I did."

A frown settled on Alida's brow.

"Let's change the subject," she said. "I don't like your talking like this, Mother."

Margaret let that pass without comment.

"*You* have the ability to love deeply," she stated after a while. "You must have inherited it from my mother, who died of a broken heart when my father was killed in a car accident—but I've told you about this before."

"You've told me about the accident, yes." Alida thought of the grandmother whom she had never known, a lady who had been so madly in love with her husband that she had nothing to live for when he was taken from her. Fortunately her children were at the stage when they could take care of themselves, one of them, Lucie, being already married with a child. Marcelle.... She had suspected that Alida was expecting a child, but she would never know whether or not her suspicions were correct. For Roger, eager to get Alida away, had insisted on an immediate marriage, and Alida had left England before her condition had really become apparent. Margaret had had some of her family over from time to time, but they were still uninformed about Alida's affairs; they still did not know of her marriage, or of the birth of the baby. The divorce had been kept quiet in spite of its being defended.

Alida recalled that last visit from Aunt Lucie and Marcelle. They had come on their own, Uncle Fred preferring to go on a golfing holiday with his friends. Marcelle had never married and she was twenty-nine now. She had never changed, either, and Roger declared emphatically that he would not have her over again. With Alida she had been spiteful and unfriendly; she was jealous of her beauty and envious of her position as the stepdaughter of a wealthy man who could give her so much.

Alida glanced up as her mother rose from her chair.

"I'm going for a swim," she said. "Are you coming?"

"In a few minutes. I'm enjoying the quiet, and the smell of flowers, and the birds, especially the hummingbirds. They're fascinating the way they hover."

Margaret looked down at her.

"Sometimes I feel there's a lot of the Cypriot in you, Alida," she said. "They live close to nature, and you are keenly interested in all things natural."

Alida nodded her head.

"That's why I want to keep this island as it is. It would be terrible if the birds were driven away because of high-rise hotels and condominiums."

"You're an idealist, sweet," declared her mother, smiling affectionately. "You make me feel I've lost a lot somewhere along the line." She turned and walked away, her svelte body moving in a way that would be the envy of an experienced model. She had everything, thought Alida—youth, for although she was forty-six she looked, and felt, no more than thirty. She had poise and assurance, and vitality. She could sail her husband's yacht; she played golf and tennis; she swam in the sea every morning without fail and sometimes in the afternoon. Yes, mused Alida, watching until she reached the shore, she had everything—even a rich and handsome husband who adored her.

After sitting there for another ten minutes or so Alida rose and strolled across the lawn and down to the private stretch of beach belonging to Mangrove Lodge. Out from the Cay were two tiny islets, the tops of mounds of underwater coral limestone, and to the east lay an atoll, a sanctuary for seabirds, especially cormorants, frigate birds and blue herons. Other, larger islands rose out of the clear cerulean ocean, their beaches fringed by palms.

The beach on this part of Coral Cay was a green palisade of palm trees sweeping away towards the thickly wooded region to the south, where the coastline curved and where, a short while ago, some rich speculator from New York had tried for permission to build a multi-storey hotel and apartment complex. Objections from the residents had succeeded and the man had sold the land for much less than he had paid, and everyone declared that it served him right for even thinking of spoiling the coastline of such a beautiful island as Coral Cay.

"Come on in!" called her mother as Alida appeared before her view. "It's gorgeous!"

"All right." Alida moved slowly, with a sylph-like grace that made it seem she glided rather than walked. Yes, it was gorgeous! Warm and smooth and caressing as a gown of silk. She swam about for a while before turning on her back and floating, her hands clasped behind her head. The sky, blue and cloudless, was dazzling in the sunshine; the low-rise buildings inland glowed orange and saffron and peach-pearl, like great semi-precious stones showering off reflected coloured lights.

"I'm coming in, girls, so get ready for the splash!"

"Vance!" Alida turned and swam for the shore. She looked up as she reached him, thinking that although she professed always not to be interested in men, Vance did at times have an attraction for her. He was tall and handsome in a rugged sort of way, with light brown hair and a sort of pale bronze complexion which matched it admirably. He was in swimming trunks and had a towel over one arm. "I'd no idea you were over. Are your father and mother with you?"

"They'll be over on Friday. Mother's throwing a party on Thursday and I just couldn't face the crowd she cultivates. If I'd deliberately gone out somewhere she'd have complained, so I said I wasn't feeling too good and I'd benefit from a few days on Coral Cay—so here I am!"

"It's nice to see you," said Alida, with a smile, glancing round to find that her mother had swum farther out from the shore, towards the surf-laced reef.

"I've just had lunch at the hotel and received something of a shock."

"A shock?" Alida had picked up the towel which her mother had left on the beach, but it remained idle in her hands. "What sort of a shock?"

"That land at the end there's been sold again, to some foreigner from Greece or somewhere like that, and it's rumoured that he's got permission to build—"

"To build!" Alida exclaimed in dismay. "But how can he? I mean, we've not had any indication, no time to put forward our objections."

"Well, he's pulled a fast one, if the rumours are to be taken seriously—and I'm pretty sure they are, Alida," he added grimly, his glance going automatically to the place in question.

"I still don't see how he's managed to get permission to build without the knowledge of the residents. What's he going to build, do you know?"

"A massive hotel and shopping plaza. And apartments, probably, the sort of inferior properties that are rented cheaply, so we'll have hordes of tourists swarming in from all over the place."

"We've no airport," returned Alida, "so that'll be a great drawback to any heavy influx of people." She thought of the method by which the people of the island got to Florida. It was a case of a water-taxi to one of the larger cays, then a small aeroplane to Nassau, and from there one took a larger plane to the mainland. "I don't think he'll do this building, Vance, because—"

"Steady on," he said, breaking into what she was saying. "He's intending to build an airstrip suited to the smaller type of aeroplane."

"No!" She looked at him aghast. "We don't want aeroplanes on a tiny island like this, Vance!"

"I'm afraid we'll have to resign ourselves to just that," was his swift rejoinder. "This man's very wealthy—inherited a few millions from his father some years ago—and he has influence, apparently. It's said that he's even now negotiating for more land here."

"More? Where?"

Vance's hesitation was more than sufficient to set her nerves fluttering, and this created a sinking feeling in the pit of her stomach.

"Clearwater Cove," he said reluctantly at last.

Alida's mouth quivered and for a few seconds she could not speak.

"My favourite place," she whispered huskily. "Oh, but no one—just no one!—would build there!"

"Sorry to be the bearer of bad news, Alida," said Vance, plainly distressed by her quivering lips and the grey pallor that had taken the place of the healthy glow in her cheeks.

"I can't believe it...." Her eyes were moist and Vance turned away from the grief in their depths. This girl was a mere child, he thought, and a child who had suffered. Oh, yes, he had guessed from the moment he met her that she had known a deep, deep suffering which had left its mark even though most people would never notice. For she had all her mother's poised assurance and ability to laugh; she appeared on the surface to be invulnerable to the pricks of life...but Vance knew for sure that her defences were weak. This stricken look on her face was proof enough, he thought. "Will the owner sell him the land, do you think? I'm referring to Clearwater Cove."

"I was talking to Sam Walsh—he's over at present, but you probably know?" Alida nodded dumbly and Vance went on to say that Sam had told him that the deal over the land at Clearwater Cove might already have gone through, as it was over a week since he had heard about it. He was in Florida at the time and there seemed to be a fair bit of interest among some of the businessmen there who dealt in real estate, since some of them had already bought land on Coral Cay and if this Greek could get building permission, then he was laying the way open for them to follow suit.

"But the whole island will be nothing but buildings!" exclaimed Alida, on the point of tears.

"Buildings and beaches," corrected Vance. And he shrugged his shoulders. "There are many very popular holiday spots that are no more than multi-storey hotel blocks and beaches."

"This man...he's Greek, you say? Why should a Greek come here, wanting to spoil our island?" she demanded furiously. "They've hundreds of islands of their own they can spoil!"

"I believe he's not altogether Greek—" Vance broke off and frowned. "He's still at the Fair Dawning, so I'll dine there this evening and find out some more about him." He paused a moment and then, "Like to come with me?" he invited. "We could dance—" He stopped and for a long moment there was silence between them. It was Alida who eventually broke it by saying,

"Yes, Vance, I'd love to come with you. What time do you want me to be ready?

She dressed carefully in a long evening gown of turquoise silk trimmed at the neckline and cuffs with an abundance of embroidery worked in silver thread. Down the front of the bodice were tiny buttons and loops with which to fasten them, both done in the same silver thread, and the cuffs were matching. The dress was styled in a Grecian line with a full flowing swing of both bodice and skirt and the sleeves coming up from below the waist, very full, their drapes adding to the many lovely folds formed by the dress itself. Roger had had it made for her in Tangier, where he had gone on business a few months ago. It was a model of sheer perfection and on the few occasions when she had worn it Alida had found herself being stared at in open-eyed admiration.

"You stop the show every time you wear it!" Roger had said proudly. "I'm very glad I bought it for you, honey!"

Vance just stood and gazed for a full twenty seconds before voicing his admiration. Alida blushed, lifted one side of the skirt so she would not trip over it, and said lightly,

"If you're ready, Vance, we'll go."

He laughed and took her arm.

"Shy of compliments, aren't you? Alida, my girl, I think I shall have to ask you to marry me! I'll find a romantic spot and propose on my knees in a proper manner—"

"Don't bother," she laughed. "You've already proposed, in the most unromantic manner, and any repetition—be it on your knees or not—would be an anticlimax!"

They got into the car and drove through an avenue of Royal palms interspersed with flamboyant trees until, reaching the gate, they turned into the road and followed the waterfront for a mile and a half before turning into the wide entrance of the Fair Dawning Hotel. Margaret had been invited to accompany them but had refused. She had letters to write, she maintained, but Alida was not deceived. Her mother always did leave her daughter alone with Vance whenever the opportunity arose.

Stopping the car on the wide space provided, Vance turned to Alida and said, his voice serious now and quietly, persuasive,

"Well, have you an answer, Alida—the answer I'd be very happy to hear?"

She shook her head and sighed.

"I don't love you, Vance," she told him. "Perhaps one day...."

"Not very encouraging," he said with a sort of grim humour. "I shall hope, of course, but I rather think I'll hope in vain."

She looked at him, and a lovely smile lit her eyes.

"You're nice," she said, "and if it's any consolation to you—there isn't anyone else."

"Well, that's something—although I suppose I already knew there was no one else." He reached for her hand and brought it to his lips in a little gesture of gallantry and friendliness. "Come on, honey, let's go in and enjoy our dinner and dancing."

"I want to take a look at this man who's trying to buy

the land," she reminded him, as if to warn him that she would not be enjoying herself this evening anywhere near as much as she had enjoyed other evenings of dining and dancing at the Fair Dawning Hotel.

CHAPTER SIX

IT was inevitable that she should be a sensation in a dress that did so much for her beauty. And the self-confidence she had acquired in the years since she left Cyprus only added to the impression of regal elegance and exquisite taste. Every head turned as she entered on the arm of her escort, and although she coloured it was only slightly, just enough to add further enhancement to an incredibly beautiful face.

Vance, debonair and smart in a tropical suit and white frilled shirt, was inordinately proud to be with her; and his attentiveness towards her was all part of this pride. He ushered her towards a table in the lounge and after seeing her seated took a chair himself and beckoned for a waiter from whom he ordered their aperitifs.

Alida glanced all around. There were not many people in the lounge, but she saw through the wide arch separating it from the restaurant that a number of tables were already occupied.

"He's not in here," Vance informed her, guessing at her reason for her swift examination of the people in the room. "He might be dining, but they say he's a strange, morose kind of man who keeps himself to himslf, and he could be dining in his room."

"I wish Roger were here," she sighed. "He'd tackle the man and demand to know what he was up to."

"Don't worry about it too much," he advised. "As I said, it's rumour—"

"Rumour usually has some foundation, Vance; you know that."

He nodded and sighed, then asked what her mother thought about it all.

"I expect she'll be phoning your father and telling him of the rumour."

"She tried to phone immediately I told her, but Roger was out, which was to be expected as he's got several big deals going through at present."

"He's a busy man, like my dad—" Vance stopped abruptly, and as she noticed the changed expression on his face Alida was suddenly conscious of the nerve-twisting sensation of impalpable tremors running along her spine. She turned her head slowly, as if being forced against her will, turned to see what had caused Vance to stop speaking.

She scarcely heard him say, "This is the man, coming into the room now," scarcely heard or saw anything except the little gasp that issued from her lips and the tall dark figure who, having entered the room through the high wide doorway, was standing, still as a statue, looking round, as if debating where to sit.

And then he gave a swift spasmodic start as his eyes lit on Alida. She froze and stiffened, her body ice from head to toe.

But the sensation was fleeting; she soon regained her composure, remembering that she had nothing to fear from him now. He was nothing to her—nothing.

He moved at last, and came towards her. She turned her head away from those staring black eyes and met those of her companion.

"You look as if you've seen a ghost," he said frowningly. "Do you know the man?"

"I was—acquainted with him—once," she managed to say, her mouth stiff but her voice fluid and almost light. "I expect he's recognised me."

"Undoubtedly. He's coming...."

"Good evening, Alida. What a pleasant surprise to meet you here." Having overcome his surprise, Darius was perfectly in control of any emotion that might be affecting him, and his tone was lukewarm. "Are you here on holiday?"

"I live here," she answered briefly, before, in a voice of cool civility, she introduced him to Vance. The two men shook hands and Vance, considering it incumbent on him to do so, invited him to join them, which he did, the slight inclination of his head an acknowledgement of the invitation as he took possession of a vacant chair opposite to where his former wife was sitting.

"Just imagine you two knowing one another!" Vance threw Alida a significant glance as if to say that perhaps she could do something to dissuade this foreigner from exploiting the island. "When did you meet—and where?"

It was Darius's turn to look at Alida, and she saw the glimmer of a sardonic smile touch the corner of his lips.

It was inevitable that, on occasions, she had visualised a meeting with her ex-husband and wondered what she would be like. At first she had known that she would feel hot with humiliation and embarrassment, but the passing years with their gifts of confidence and maturity had brought the knowledge that she would be more than capable of holding her own with him. But she had reckoned without the passing years having given him something too; all she had seen in her imagination was the youth who had married her, a rather blustering youth who was filled with a sense of his own superiority and whose inherited traits had included a somewhat primitive uncouthness which was apparent even though he had been given a superior education and was the son of the island's wealthiest man.

Yes, she mused as she looked at him across the table, she had certainly reckoned without the changes that the years had brought about.

"We met in Cyprus," she heard Darius saying in answer to Vance's question. "It was eight years ago, at an engagement ceremony first and then, later, at a wedding." His eyes were fixed upon her face with a steely intentness that revealed nothing of his feelings; in fact, apart from the expression in his eyes his face was a mask. Alida flushed slightly but soon recovered. She had not been the stepdaughter of a man like Roger for eight years without learning how to maintain her dignity. She had also learned quite a lot about retaliation. Always give as good as you get, was Roger's advice, and, remembering this, she said, in that fluid tone and with the trace of a smile,

"Yes, I remember very well, Mr. Valaris. The girl had been forced into an arranged marriage by her father. The wedding took place only a week after the engagement ceremony. The girl, only seventeen years old, had seen the man only once before the day of her wedding." She was watching him, waiting for the arrogant lift of his brows or the compression of his mouth. She saw neither; his face was still a mask.

"Forced?" echoed Vance perplexedly. "How could she be forced into marriage? Are you saying it was against her will?"

"Very much against her will," returned Alida, glanc-

ing at him. "In Cyprus and in Greece and other coun-
tries of the East, the female is considered as inferior.
From birth till death she's usually under male control of
some kind. In the case in question the girl was coerced
into marriage by her father because the man who
became her husband saw her, desired her, and offered
for her."

"And she was married to him, after seeing him only
twice!" exclaimed Vance, shaking his head in disbelief.

"Yes, she was married to a stranger," returned Alida,
marvelling at the cool detached quality of her voice. It
was as if she were talking about someone else—just as
Vance believed she was—and not about herself at all.

"Good God!" Vance looked across at Darius, deep
disgust in his eyes. "This sort of thing happens in your
part of the world? What an antiquated set-up! It seems
impossible that such customs can survive in this day and
age!"

"Unfortunately they do," began Alida, then stopped
as one of the waiters, having been hailed by Vance, went
by without coming to take Darius's order. Vance rose at
once to go to the bar himself. He asked what Darius was
having, then asked Alida if she would like another
drink. She shook her head at once, reminding him that
they would be drinking a bottle of wine shortly and if
she had another drink she would be "heady" before she
started on her wine. He laughed and went away. Darius
and Alida were alone. . . .

They looked at one another for a long moment before
Darius broke the silence, saying casually,

"Doesn't your friend know you come from Cyprus?"

"I took my stepfather's name. He wanted me to and
it suited me to do so. To have your name was a burden
which I was most happy to get rid of."

"You've changed," he said. "You've become very English."

"People do change—in eight years. You yourself are very much changed."

"The sprinklings of grey, you mean?" He shrugged his shoulders indifferently. "Yes, I admit I've changed—changed in many ways."

She looked at him in silence, scarcely aware of the babble of voices around her, or the Bahamian music being played by the calypso band in the restaurant. She was mentally taking stock of the man who had been her husband for one single day. Yes, there was a change, a dramatic one and no mistake. For apart from the slight softening of his features, there was the change in his manner, in the way he conducted himself. He appeared to her now as a cultured, cultivated man of refinement and taste. He was more aloof in his bearing, punctiliously urbane in his speech. True, she had sensed a degree of cynicism about both his voice and his manner, but it was subtly controlled and she felt that had she never met him before she would not have noticed it. On the surface he was the polished aristocrat, a man of the world—very different from the arrogant, pompous young man whose knowledge of the world was confined to one small island whose inhabitants were, in the main, steeped in customs that made the Western world gasp in disbelief.

He was in full evening dress, and this added to the impression of *savoir-vivre,* that was, in reality, the most striking of the changes she saw in him. He was older, yes, and maturity had added lines to his forehead and the corners of his eyes. His hands—those big hands that had roughly caressed her—were filled out a little, and there were blue veins on the backs, markedly apparent now, his hands being clenched upon the table. He moved them as he saw her eyes come to rest on them and his own eyes went to her left hand—just as they had the moment he had come up to the table.

"I rather thought you'd have remarried in all this long time," he said.

"I haven't yet met anyone I can love."

His mouth curved cynically at her mention of love.

"Still the romantic? What of this man you are with?" Darius's voice was lukewarm again, impassive. He was not really interested in Vance and the place he might occupy in Alida's affection.

"He's a very good friend," she said, and then, her beautiful eyes softening slightly, "You, Darius—you never married, either?" She had no idea why she had phrased the question like that. But somehow she just knew that he had never remarried.

He was shaking his head. She noticed the strands of silver at the temples, attractively caught in the light.

"I've been otherwise occupied since my father's death almost eight years ago."

"Eight—" She frowned as she added, "He must have died almost immediately after...." She slid her voice to a halt and her frown deepened.

"He had a heart attack after hearing that my wife had left me." Dispassionate the tone, and no condemnation in the eyes either. Yet Alida found herself saying,

"You blame me—for his death?"

To her relief he shook his head instantly.

"It's my belief that we all go when our time comes," he said seriously. "My father would have died anyway. The sad thing was that he died a very unhappy man."

Through me, decided Alida, but kept this thought to herself. She had no regrets. It was her life she had considered, her future. Darius's father had been nothing to her and although she was sorry that he had died unhappy she had no intention of letting it trouble her unduly.

She said, glancing round to see if Vance was coming back,

"These other things that have been occupying you— they took you away from Cyprus?" It was phrased as a question but was in fact a statement, and her ex-husband smiled faintly as he replied,

"It's obvious to you that I've been away from Cyprus for some time."

"Yes, it is."

"I've been in America for several years, and before that I was in England and France. I've had a few months in Germany too, and Italy."

"You enjoy travelling, obviously." She thought: this is the most incredulous situation. Here we are, a divorced couple who have met again by a chance in a million on a tiny island in the Atlantic, and we're chatting to one another without animosity—we're almost friendly, in fact!

"It's been mainly on business."

She leant forward in her chair to take up her glass. Darius had provided the opening for her to broach the subject of the land and his projected building programme, and she sought for the right words to convey what was on her mind.

"You buy and sell land?" she said at last, recalling that he had owned vast *donums* of land covered by orange groves in Cyprus.

"I have been doing, yes," he answered. "I've acquired some land here and am intending to build an hotel. Then I shall sell it. I've a buyer waiting, as a matter of fact."

"We—we don't want an hotel on Coral Cay," she said, at once aware that whatever she should say it would have no effect on his plans regarding the hotel. But she hoped he would not be able to acquire the land at Clearwater Cove. She had an idea that she could persuade her stepfather to buy it, and that would put an end forever to any plans which Darius—or anyone else for that matter—might have regarding its potential as a building site.

"You live here, you said?"

"My parents have a home here. Roger's business is in Miami, though, so we have a house there as well. But Roger will be retiring soon and he wants to live here permanently. We don't want an hotel and hundreds of tourists. The island's not big enough." She looked at the dark angular features; they were inscrutable, as unresponsive as a statue's. He would not abandon his plans, no matter what objections the residents of Coral Cay might raise.

"As I said, I've acquired the land. The hotel is definitely going up."

Alida lifted her glass to her lips, aware of an aching sensation at the back of her throat. He was as heartless as ever, she thought, and all the bitter hatred she had felt for him during those long pain-weary months of carrying his child returned with an almost savage intensity. Yes, she hated him and always would! Already a millionaire, he would despoil this little piece of Paradise in order to get more. She said huskily at last,

"I can only hope that something happens to prevent your plans from materialising." She looked at him, noting the fine-drawn intentness of his eyes. "It would have to be a miracle," she added on a note of despair which had no effect on him at all.

"Such as my dropping dead," he murmured with irony. "It's a million to one chance, Alida, so I think you would be wasting your time wishing for it."

"I don't wish you dead."

He heard the flash in her voice and looked sceptical.

"Despite your indignation I rather think you would be relieved to hear that I had met with a fatal accident."

She shrugged and put her glass down. The ice tinkled in it and for a fleeting moment their attention was caught.

"If that's what you think, then I can't stop you," she said indifferently.

Darius changed the subject abruptly.

"You've grown very beautiful, Alida. Why is it that you aren't married?"

"I've told you—I haven't met the man I shall eventually fall in love with."

Yes, he had changed, she thought again, recalling his possessiveness, his wild uncontrolled fury when the divorce was granted, and his assertion that he would always look upon her as his lawful wife. It seemed that this idea had died a long while ago. He certainly did not consider her his wife now. His total indifference was more than enough proof of that.

"You're nearly twenty-six. You could be left on the shelf."

"I'm not a Cypriot girl with the fear of spinsterhood that they have. I'm perfectly happy as I am. It's been a good life since—" She stopped, her pulse quivering at the nearness of the slip! Darius was regarding her curiously and questioningly. "Since I found my mother," she ended, picking up her glass again and taking a sip of her drink.

"You're perfectly happy, you say?" His glance was

sceptical. "You are the sort of girl who needs fulfilment. Spinsterhood can hardly be fulfilling, can it?"

"It depends on one's interpretation of the word fulfilling. We live a good life, my parents and I. We're very lucky to be on this island...." Her voice trailed and her lower lip was caught suddenly between her teeth. "I expect Roger will find another lovely haven of peace," she quavered, glancing away and then seeing Vance coming along with two glasses in his hand.

"Thanks," said Darius briefly as one of the glasses was put before him.

"Are you dining in the restaurant, Mr. Valaris?" Vance had asked the question before realising it was superfluous. The man would scarcely dress if he was having his dinner sent up to his room.

"Yes. I was expecting a friend—he was bringing his yacht over, but something must have delayed him."

Alida cast him a swift glance. She could not have explained it, but some instinct told her that the man with the yacht was the owner of the land at Clearwater Cove.

If only she could manage to meet him before Darius did....

"Will he be over later tonight?" she asked.

Darius shrugged and said he could not say.

"However, he'll be over tomorrow some time. I shall stay here for a few days anyway—" He stopped as a waiter approached with three menus and handed them one each.

"You have some business with this man?" Alida attempted to sound merely interested in a casual way, but immediately she noticed the expression of sardonic amusement that came to his face she realised that she had not been very successful.

"Yes," he said briefly as he began to peruse the menu, "I do have some business with him."

It was Vance who invited Darius to join them for dinner. Alida did not know why he should have thought it necessary, but he told her later, when they got up to dance between the first and second courses, that he had been in a quandary, because he was not sure if Darius was a friend.

"But even if he were a mere acquaintance it wouldn't have looked very nice, letting him dine alone." He glanced down at her. "You're not pleased, are you?"

"It's just that I don't like him," she said, but added quickly that it did not matter. Vance must not worry about it. "I'm wondering if that person with the yacht is the owner of Clearwater Cove—in fact, I'm fairly sure he is."

"Did Mr. Valaris mention anything about the hotel while I was away getting the drinks?" He looked concerned and yet hopeful. Alida said flatly,

"He's definitely building. He's already got a buyer for the hotel."

"What a damned shame! How he managed to get permission beats me! He must have influence somewhere!"

"Not necessarily—in fact, I'm sure he hasn't influence. That sort of thing wouldn't get him anywhere in any case, not if the authorities decided this island was to be preserved. No, I think that the development of some of the Out Islands is planned, and you can understand that this must be so, as the economy depends on tourism in a lot of cases, but I do think they could have chosen a larger island than this."

"If we get one large hotel complex, in addition to this small one, you can bet your life we shall have a forest of concrete blocks before a couple of years have passed.''

''I agree.'' She hated Darius with a black venom! What right had he to come here with his money and plan the ruin of such a beauty spot?

Perhaps something *would* happen, though. Some miracle. But how could it? If Darius had the land already he would be building within a few weeks at the most.

Darius asked her to dance later and although she could not very well snub him by refusing she gave him that kind of a look that left him in no doubt that the idea of dancing with him was abhorrent to her. She had danced with him before. . .at her wedding. . . .

He held her close, but not uncomfortably so. She was surprised by his air of refined consideration for her feelings, and she recalled her stepfather's words—and her mother's—about the possibility of his improving with age. He *had* improved, in several ways, but he had also acquired a greed for money, a greed that had brought him here to exploit this lovely little islet and turn it into a popular resort for tourists. She wanted to cry. He had hurt her once before and now fate was allowing him to hurt her again. And she could do nothing to stop him; no one could.

But she would have a good try to stop him buying the land at Clearwater Cove!

''You're very quiet, Alida.'' His words came slowly, softly, close to her ear.

''I don't feel like talking,'' she said brusquely.

''You hate me for coming here and buying that land.'' A statement. She answered truthfully and said yes, she did hate him for buying the land.

''You could have chosen some other island,'' she added, looking up into his face. "There are larger islands where tourism is already established."

"I know. I've bought land on several of the Out Islands."

"You're a speculator, then?" It was incredible, she thought, just how great the change had been. He was clearly a confident businessman, a man who had been around and knew what he was doing.

"The same as your stepfather," he said smoothly.

She fell silent and they danced their way to the table. But, later, he asked her again, and this time the meal was finished and another couple had drifted over to their table, to sit chatting after being formally introduced to Darius. They were friends of both Alida and Vance, a man and wife who had saved for years to get the money to build a small but well-designed villa by the sea. They were semi-retired and came over to their villa about four times a year, staying about a month on each occasion.

"You appear to have some very nice friends," Darius commented, plainly for something to say, because the silence between them was fast becoming strained and Alida wondered why he had asked her to dance in the first place. Somehow, she had the impression that his action resulted from some strange compulsion which he could not control.

"You mean the Graysons? Yes, they are nice. We have them to dinner once or twice while they're here. Mr. Grayson has a small retail business which he's going to pass over to his son shortly and then they'll retire here, I expect. Mrs. Grayson also works in the business, but she hasn't been well for some months so she might stay on this time, and let her husband return to Florida on his own."

"Tell me about some of the other people who live here—or have holiday retreats here."

She lifted her face, staring at him in some surprise.

"Are you really interested?" she wanted to know, and he shrugged and said casually that it was something to talk about.

But she fell quiet, and after a while he broke the silence again by suggesting they go out on to the patio for a breath of fresh air. She stiffened momentarily, then relaxed. There was nothing to be afraid of, nor was there any reason why she should not go outside with him. She was rather warm anyway, and she knew that the air outside was cool and fresh and perfumed with the heady fragrance of frangipani and oleander and old-fashioned garden roses.

She agreed, and Darius put a hand beneath her elbow, urging her forward towards the edge of the dance area and the exit to the patio and garden where a flower-edged path led down to the beach. The moon was high, sailing in smooth silver motion through wispy cirrus clouds, platinum-lined against a deep purple sky.

They stood on the patio side by side and the silence between them became intense and suddenly everything seemed unreal to Alida, impossible, something out of a dream. She turned and spoke her thoughts involuntarily, because she had to say what was in her mind.

"Why are you here? Why has this happened? It was the most improbable thing that we should ever meet again—unless I went to Cyprus, that was. Yet here you are, in this hotel, on this tiny island so many miles away from your home. How has it happened, and why?" she said again.

"Coincidence," was his cool reply. "It's a strange thing."

She was not convinced.

"I'd rather blame fate," she said, putting out a hand to rest it on the wrought-iron rail that ran along one side of the patio.

"Blame, Alida?"

"The distressing truth is that you've come into my life to hurt me again."

He was frowning, she knew, even without looking at him.

"I didn't come here deliberately to hurt you—" He put a hand upon hers and fell silent a moment. She felt his touch surprisingly cool, like the caress of a breeze. Within her something stirred, like the quivering sensation of nerves fluttering, propelled by the subconscious mind. Unreality again; she must shake herself out of it!

"Not deliberately; I didn't accuse you of that." She twisted so that she had her back to him, but his hand continued to cover hers.

"You couldn't have suffered much from the experience of marriage to me." A slight harshness entered his voice, an alien note that raised resentment within her. "You weren't married long enough for that."

Not suffered.... How little he knew! Should she tell him about their dead baby? The idea was cast aside at once. She had never deliberately hurt anyone in her life and she would not start now. All she said was,

"You can't say how much, or how little, my suffering was, because you are a man and men don't *feel* as deeply as women."

"I admit it," he said, and she went on,

"It so happens that the wound went deep—" She turned to face him, drawing her hand from under his. In the thread of candlelight from the room behind her he saw the strain and darkness in her eyes, but for all that there was a rare sweetness and serenity about her face, an appealing attraction in the full sensitive mouth. Watching him, Alida saw with a little start of surprise and fascination that a muscle was moving spasmodically in his throat, and she wondered at the reason for it because it seemed to depict a weakness which was totally at variance with the iron-hard grimness of his features— the chiselled jawline and firm determined mouth and chin, the piercing eyes so intently fixed upon her, their dark depths inscrutable as those of a pagan god carved in stone.

He had changed, she thought yet again. . .and the pic- ture that had been engraved on her mind for years—that of the arrogant youth who had fathered her child—was gone for ever and she was left floundering in a strange void, because this man was certainly not the man who had fathered her dead baby. "I would have gone under if it hadn't been for Roger and my mother...." Her voice trailed as she realised that she had mentioned her stepfather first. Yet she had always known that she loved him more than she loved her mother, not because of what he had done for her financially, but for the love and affection and friendship he had given her. "They were marvellous to me and I shall never be able to repay them."

"Your mother's help was rather belated, don't you think?" he said drily and with a grimness coming to his eyes.

"That's all in the past, Darius," she returned simply.

"As our little affair is all in the past." He seemed tired all at once and she asked if he wanted to go back inside. He shook his head and flicked a hand towards the silent shore.

"I'm taking a walk along there," he said and, after

an uncertain moment, "You'd not want to come with me, I suppose?"

She shook her head at once. The talcum-soft sand on a moon-placid shore, the drowsy lagoon in the starlight, palms swaying against a night-purple sky, and the soft gentle music of water cascading over the reef.... This was for lovers, the setting for romance and kisses and the heady sensation that heaven itself was only a breath away. She shook her head again and said she was going back to her friends. Darius inclined his head in a gesture of acceptance and the next moment he was walking slowly away from her, and although she wanted to move she could not. It was as if some compelling force prevented movement, directed her to remain where she was until he was out of sight. He seemed so lonely! A man without any real purpose in life. She fell to wondering just how he had used those years since his father died. He had entered into the world of business, and so he must have learned a good deal about life in the West, about things which would have convinced him that the notions instilled by generations of his ancestors were not always right for everyone, and that the idea of male arrogance and superiority had no place in the culture of Western society. Had he been back to Cyprus since he left? she wondered.

She frowned suddenly, aware that she was taking far too much interest in the man she had always hated. If he was lonely he deserved to be! In any case, there was always a remedy: he could get married. She supposed there were many women who would be glad to marry a millionaire...and he was handsome, in a severe and rather forbidding way. Some women would like the severity of his manner and his appearance, would delight in being mastered—but not of course dominated or oppressed like some of the women of his particular part of the world. Yes, he could get married, and have children. He would not be lonely, then. Her eyes continued to follow him until he stopped suddenly and stood staring out to sea. Alida frowned and an involuntary sigh issued from her lips. Why should she be feeling sorry for him, after the way he had made her suffer? Impatience soon took the place of her pity. If only he had not come here. Well, as long as he had come, it would be a good thing when he had finished what he came for, and he then took himself off again.

She turned at last, to enter the room where candles and flowers and soft Bahamian music made the setting for the quiet conversations taking place among the people sitting in the lounge. But as she stepped into the room something made her glance round again. Darius was still there, a dark silhouette against a background of sea and sky, a man alone, estranged from the world. . . .

What an odd impression! And yet it persisted. It was as if she had learned suddenly that he had turned in on himself, that although in business he was forced to mix, in his private life he preferred to be alone. . . .

CHAPTER SEVEN

ALIDA was on the telephone at half-past eight the following morning, ringing her stepfather. Her mother was still in bed; she had a tummy upset, she told Alida when, after taking her early morning bathe, she looked into Margaret's luxurious blue and white bedroom to ask if she was joining her for breakfast.

"No, dear; get yours and then ring your father. He must come over—at once!"

Reflecting on her mother's reaction when, having been brought home by Vance, she had related the dramatic events of the evening, Alida was extremely perplexed by the fact that the news she had imparted had disturbed Margaret even more than it had disturbed her daughter. And it seemed that it was not merely the fact that Darius was in this part of the world and was intending to build an hotel complex which troubled her. There was something else, a sort of fear almost, thought Alida, noticing her mother's scared expression and the extreme pallor of her face that made it seem almost milky white.

"Roger..." Alida spoke his name on a low, affectionate note. "It's something most important that I've rung you about," she continued without preamble. And she then went on to explain what had happened.

"He's already managed to get some land, Father," she added when he did not speak. "But it's Clearwater

Cove that's worrying us now—well, it's worrying me, for I love it as you know. Roger, can you buy it before he manages to do so?''

Roger was clearly staggered and it was some moments before he could speak. He promised to do what he could; he'd be over before lunch if he could get a plane to one of the large Out Islands and then the boat to Coral Cay.

''You think that the owner will be there later today?'' he added, and it was plain by the tone of his voice that he was deep in thought, trying to remember who owned Clearwater Cove.

''Darius was supposed to meet someone from a yacht, but he didn't turn up. I somehow had the impression that this man was the owner, but of course I'm not sure. It was only guesswork on my part.''

''Well, we shall soon know. I'll be with you just as soon as I can.''

Alida went along to tell her mother what had transpired.

''I do hope he can get a plane! Oh, I've never before realised just how cut off we are here!'' Margaret was sitting up in bed, beautiful and alluring in a nightgown of seductively diaphanous material. Her hair looked immaculate and it was plain that she had been out of bed to comb it.

''There's nothing we can do to speed things on,'' returned Alida, but did add that she was going to see if the man had arrived, and if he had she would make it her business to have a talk to him and inform him that he might get a better offer for the land if he would care to wait a short while.

''It's only conjecture that this yachtsman's the owner of the land,'' said Margaret with a sigh. She seemed distant, uncommunicative, as if she were immersed in some thoughts which she had no intention of making known to her daughter.

"I know, but if my hunch does happen to be right we might be able to prevent Darius from buying the land at Clearwater Cove."

She left the villa a few minutes later, making for the marina. There were several yachts there which weren't there yesterday and she stood and frowned, her eyes wandering from one to the other. Impossible to say which one it might be, and in any case her idea was only a hunch, as she had said to her mother.

"So we meet again." A smooth expressionless voice made her turn swiftly. The colour rose to her cheeks and tinglings ran along her spine.

"Darius... you're out early." She was flustered, unsure of herself. Where, she wondered, was her cool composure, the self-possession she had acquired during the past few years?

"Early?" he said with a slight lift of his straight black brows. "It's almost nine o'clock."

"People are usually having breakfast at this time."

"You aren't having breakfast."

"No... well, I had something to do." Automatically her eyes wandered to one of the yachts, then moved to another.

"Such as?"

Alida gave a shrug of her shoulders.

"Just something," she replied. "It wouldn't interest you," she added, lowering her eyes in case she should give away the fact that she was lying.

"I'm meeting a friend, but he hasn't arrived yet—" Darius stopped abruptly, as if vexed that he should have spoken in a confiding way. Alida said quietly,

"Is your friend the owner of Clearwater Cove?"

He gave a slight start but recovered immediately.

"What made you refer to Clearwater Cove?" he asked, watching her closely.

"I've heard that you're thinking of buying some land there." A dryness caught her throat and affected her voice so that there was a distinct catch in it. Darius was still intently watching her face, the most odd expression in his eyes.

"You have some special reason why you don't want a house at Clearwater Cove?" Smooth the tone and yet something in it that was unfathomable...and significantly profound.

She looked up into his nobly-chiselled face and thought it possessed all the arrogance of a Greek god. How different he was! Alida could not help but remember him as he was—the inexperienced youth with a vision so narrowed that he had not for one moment imagined that she would be anything other than filled with gratitude that he had offered for her—he, the son of one of Cyprus's wealthiest men, saving her from spinsterhood. His arrogance at that time was bumptious, impudent; he was clumsy, trying to appear polished and failing miserably. But now.... His whole demeanour and appearance were the embodiment of refinement and cultivated taste. He seemed far, far above her, and the idea brought two bright spots of angry colour to Alida's cheeks. Yet when she spoke in answer to his question there was about her a sort of warm simplicity and calmness that affected him profoundly.

"Yes, Darius," she said quietly, "I do have some special reason for not wanting a house to be built on Clearwater Cove. You see, it's my favourite place; it's where I go when I want to be quite alone, with my thoughts—" She broke off because of the lump in her throat and because of the cloud of tears that had gathered behind her eyes. Darius seemed deeply affected, but he frowned presently and told her that he had already acquired the land at Clearwater Cove and that his friend was coming over merely to finalise the deal.

"He is the man whom I mentioned last night," admitted Darius. "You had obviously guessed."

Her lip quivered and she turned away. He stood looking down at the top of her head for a long moment before speaking.

"I'm building a house there for myself."

Alida swung around.

"For yourself?" She shook her head in sheer dismay. "You're intending to live here, on Coral Cay?"

"Yes, Alida, I am."

"You can't!" she cried fiercely. "What do you want to live here for? You're miles away from home!"

"So are you," he reminded her suavely. And, when she found no answer to that, "There's room enough on this island for both of us, Alida."

"No! No, there isn't! I don't want you here, so close! Why, I'd see you every single day!"

Faintly he smiled...and seemed all at once to become inordinately attractive. She frowned inwardly; she was uneasy because of the fact that she *could* find him attractive. She ought to be hating him, not only for what he had done in the past but for what he intended doing to her now.

"I'm sorry if the sight of me offends you," he said urbanely. "But I can't change my plans because of that. I intend to live here permanently, and if it doesn't suit you you know what you can do." And with that he turned and strode away, his tall lithe figure soon lost to view as he reached the wooded area which backed on to the waterfront.

There were tears in her eyes when she walked into the villa to find her mother having a light breakfast of toast and coffee.

"What's wrong?" Margaret seemed edgy, strung up. "You look ready to weep!"

"I am ready to weep."

Margaret frowned heavily.

"Well, for goodness' sake tell me why!"

Alida swallowed.

"Darius is building himself a house at Clearwater Cove."

Silence. Margaret's hand shook visibly.

"No.... It isn't true! He can't live here!"

Alida's eyes narrowed slightly as they fixed themselves on her mother's trembling hand.

"Is something wrong? I mean—you look terrified."

Margaret pulled herself together.

"Terrified?" she repeated, her eyes opening to their full extent. "Why on earth should I be terrified?"

"I don't know, but you did seem afraid." She was thoughtful, remembering last night and the way her mother had received the news of Darius's arrival on Coral Cay. There was fear in her eyes—yes, Alida was sure of it. And yet what could frighten her? Darius could not possibly harm her, no more than he could harm Alida herself.

"I wonder if Roger'll manage to get here." Margaret buttered herself another piece of toast and took a bite out of it. She looked at Alida, noting the gleaming dark hair which contrasted with the pale golden skin of her face, the thickly-fringed eyes of brown beneath delicately-arched brows, the rosy lips that had parted in a smile at the mention of Roger's name. The girl adored him, thought Margaret, and for a fleeting moment she knew a tinge of pique. But it passed and was forgotten; she was glad that her husband and her daughter got on so well together.

"I expect he'll get here," said Alida with confidence, "but of course he can't do anything about the land. It's too late—it was too late when I phoned him, because Darius had already acquired the land."

"It's disastrous, Alida. We can't live here once he takes up residence."

"No, I agree. Roger will be so grieved; he'd set his heart on living here when he retired."

Alida was still puzzled by her mother's attitude, for although she was contriving to appear cool now and had successfully erased all sign of fear from her eyes, Alida was convinced that she was deeply perturbed in some indefinable way.

"It's a mystery," she sighed as she went out on to the terrace and stood looking appreciatively over the gardens to the lagoon. But it was to become a bigger mystery later when Roger arrived. He had seemed cool, offhand, with Alida for the first time that she could remember, and after giving her a perfunctory kiss and a swift hug he disappeared into the house where Margaret was waiting for him in the sitting-room. Alida, affected by the strange misgivings that were as disturbing as they were inexplicable, sought peace and solitude in a little arbour sheltered by drooping fern trees and willows. She had not been there more than a few minutes when she heard voices and realised that Roger and her mother were walking along the path on the other side of the shrubbery. She thought she would join them and rose from her seat. But Margaret's voice came to her and she stiffened on the instant as she heard her say, in a high-pitched tone that held a distinct note of agitation and fear,

"Supposing he should find out!"

"He can't, dear. I keep on telling you." Impatience in Roger's voice despite its tenderness. "It's impossible simply because they don't live in this part of the world."

"Not the Bahamas, no, but in Florida! It's near enough for—"

"Rubbish, my darling. You're worrying unnecessarily...!" Roger's voice faded and Alida was left bewilderedly wondering what the conversation was all about. She felt sure that it concerned Darius and his presence on Coral Cay, but on the other hand she could not for the life of her fathom why her mother should be in such a panic—for undoubtedly she was in a panic—or why should she have used the expression,

"Supposing he should find out!"

A sigh escaped Alida and for a moment she felt like going out and joining them, just to see what would happen. But she guessed instinctively that her mother would shut up like a clam, since what she had to say was obviously for her husband's ears alone.

It was a quarter of an hour later that they all met on the terrace, over afternoon tea. Roger seemed depressed, but he stated quite categorically that he would not think of selling Mangrove Lodge yet because he felt that Darius would never settle in the house he was building at Clearwater Cove.

"He's a speculator and he'll build to sell."

Margaret did not share his confidence.

"He's a changed man, from what Alida says, and I can't imagine him saying one thing and meaning another."

"You may be right," conceded Roger, but went on to add that he himself was not going to make any hasty moves until he knew exactly what was happening. At this Alida noticed her mother's agitation. She had been drinking her tea, but she put the cup down on the saucer and seemed to become lost in thought.

"I'd like to live in our other house, Roger," she said persuasively. "And I'm sure that Alida would be much more comfortable away from here."

Roger shook his head firmly.

"Alida has nothing to worry about," he returned in a calm unhurried voice. "That man upset her life once, but he can't possibly upset it again."

How little he knew, Alida was thinking a fortnight later when, after running into Darius more than a dozen times, because the island was so small, she began to realise—both to her amazement and disbelief—that she was becoming more and more aware of him as a man, of his undeniable attractions, of his meticulous attention to manners and etiquette. She and Vance had had his company at the dinner table on three occasions and he was all concern for Alida's comfort. He danced with her on many occasions and his conversation was charming. Was he trying to make up a little for what he had done to her? she often wondered. Undoubtedly he now knew that arranged marriages were not always right. He had admitted it, which surprised her. Yet on the other hand the admission was in keeping with the changed man that he had become since his father's death.

The hotel was not started, but some materials had arrived—great piles of bricks and bags of cement. A bulldozer had been brought by boat and was ready to clear the beautiful trees from the land. To all the residents it was heartbreaking, and the more Alida examined her own feelings the more she despised herself for being attracted to the man who was responsible for all this unhappiness. She had told herself over and over again that she ought to be hating him...but she had to own that what was creeping into her heart was something far, far removed from hatred.

Vance had again asked her to marry him, but she had refused. She liked him well enough, and both Roger and Margaret had urged her to think seriously about marriage to him. However, Roger became very understanding and now never even mentioned the idea of her marrying Vance. Margaret was more persistent, and every now and then she would put in a hint about Vance's attractiveness, his wealth, his standing both here and in Miami.

"He's a good catch, love." Margaret was reading a letter as she spoke and Alida felt the words were automatic, said for the sake of breaking the silence. She and Alida were breakfasting on the patio, where the sun-drenched colour of the garden was their immediate view—the red and golden roses in one border and the white and orange in another, the wistaria tumbling in delightful abandon over a wall that had been built from gleaming white coral limestone. There were mimosa and bougainvillea, hibiscus, and oleander and a dozen other tropical delights. Over it all was the clear sapphire sky, with the spidery tracing of palm fronds making patterns as the breeze moved them gently against it.

"A good catch he might be, Mother, but I don't happen to be in love with him."

"Hmm...." A slight frown was appearing on Margaret's smooth forehead.

"What is it? What has Aunt Lucie to say?"

"Oh, she gives me all the news, as usual. But it's Marcelle—she wants to come over for a holiday, soon."

Alida caught her mother's frown.

"Roger won't be pleased if she comes," she said.

"He swore he'd never have her again, but I really don't see how we're going to get out of it." Margaret picked up her coffee cup and regarded her daughter from over the rim. "She was just impossible with you, darling—showed her envy all the time. And even before we came here, when we were in England, she gave you a pretty rough time, didn't she?"

Alida nodded her head.

"Yes, she did," she returned reflectively. Marcelle had plainly regarded her cousin as a potential rival for the affection of David who right from the first had been interested in Alida. When she left after the hurried marriage of her mother and Roger David swore he would come over to Miami and see her, but he had never mentioned it since, and after the first couple of letters he had not even bothered to write to his aunt or to Alida. Alida thought that he might turn his attention to Marcelle, but both he and she were still unmarried.

"I shall have to consult Roger," Margaret was saying. "I'm very much afraid we shall have to let Marcelle come over because there isn't any reason for putting her off."

Roger arrived at the week-end and was told of the contents of the letter. He was against Marcelle's visit, but had to agree with his wife that it was impossible to write back to Lucie and say her daughter could not come.

"She'll be arriving on the mail boat on Friday," Alida heard her mother say a fortnight later when she was talking to Roger on the pool patio that looked out on to the lagoon and the fringing reef. "Alida can go and meet her—"

"I'd rather you came with me," interrupted Alida quickly. "I never feel at ease with her in spite of the fact that I'm no longer the shy little Cypriot girl I was when I first met her. On her last visit to us here she and I didn't get on, as you very well know."

"It's her manners," frowned Roger. "There's nothing at all nice about Marcelle in my opinion, nothing whatsoever to recommend her."

"Except her beauty," inserted his wife. "She's devastating, Roger; even you will have to agree about that."

"Surface beauty," he said with derision, his eyes affectionately seeking his stepdaughter's face. "Alida has it underneath as well."

She coloured, but daintily and without any real embarrassment. Roger was always lavish in his praise and with his compliments, so Alida was used to hearing him comment on her looks and her character.

"Have you seen Darius?" enquired Margaret, changing the subject.

"Yes, several times this week." Her colour heightened and it *was* embarrassment this time, because of her inner feelings and admissions and the whirlpool of questions that flitted through her brain. She was asking herself why hatred had dissolved when it should be increasing; she asked why her emotions were aroused in the way they were on every occasion of her meeting with her former husband. And now, at the mere mention of his name by her mother she found her pulse had quickened.

"Does he speak to you?"

"Of course." Alida hoped she sounded casual but was still aware of the warm colour in her cheeks. She had not told either her mother or Roger that she had seen Darius many times recently or that she had dined in his company, and danced with him. "It's impossible for us to ignore one another on an island of this size."

"I haven't met him once." Margaret's voice was expressionless, but Alida's quick ears caught the note of uneasiness in it. The fear she had evinced at first was no longer there, but it was something which had impressed Alida so strongly that, in her conversation with Darius, she had several times tried to elicit some information that would throw a gleam of light on the matter but she had failed.

"Nor have I," from Roger, "and I don't want to. It's his intention to ruin this island and nothing anyone can do will stop him."

Alida said nothing, but that evening when she and Vance were in conversation with Darius he said a strange thing.

"I'm coming to like this island enormously, and I feel it must not be spoilt."

Alida stared in disbelief. No longer was Darius the hard unfeeling businessman who had at first said that if his plans for building did not suit her, then she knew what she could do.

"You mean—that you might reconsider, and not build here after all?" Emotion and hope heightened the tenor of her voice, but it was still sweet. And Darius seemed oddly affected by it and for a long moment he seemed lost in thought...pleasant thought. Did he like her? Alida's pulse quickened as the question emerged from her subconscious. Yes, she realised, deep within her subconscious she was hoping that he would come to like her.

It was incredible—but true!

"I've already sold the hotel I'm planning to build," he said quietly, his accent seeming very foreign to her at this moment—foreign and yet attractive.

Vance and Alida exchanged glances, and it seemed that Vance was about to speak, but at that moment he was hailed unceremoniously by a friend and with a murmured word of apology he got up and went over to him. Alida took up her glass but merely held it, moving the amber contents so that they caught the light from a wall lamp above her head. They were in the old slave kitchen that was now an intimate and intriguing bar with a timbered roof and massive stone fireplace where the slaves' food was once cooked.

At last she said, breaking the silence that had stretched without becoming tensed or strained,

"You're quite determined, then, to build the hotel?"

He made no immediate reply, his dark eyes faintly brooding and narrowed.

"As I said, the hotel already has a buyer. I should lose a considerable sum of money if I were to break the contract we've made."

Alida paused, considering his words and having to agree that the decision not to build would be an extremely foolish one. She felt sure that her stepfather—were he placed in a similar position—would not dream of changing his mind.

"Clearwater Cove," she murmured at length, deciding to leave the matter of the hotel. "You're going through with the building of the house?"

"Yes, Alida, I am," he replied, and there was no hesitation this time. It was plain that he was in no doubt about that decision. "It's your favourite place on the island, you once said?" His voice was low, with an unfathomable inflection in its depths. Alida found herself looking at him intently, trying to read what was in his eyes.

"It is my favourite place, yes," she said, and at the quaver in her tone he frowned and a small sigh issued from his lips.

"I promise you I shall not spoil Clearwater Cove, Alida."

"Any building would spoil it."

"I don't agree. I'm intending to build a very beautiful house."

"For yourself?"

He looked at her; she felt he was taking in every single thing about her face, her eyes, her hair. It seemed an age before he answered her.

"For myself at first, yes."

"At first?"

"I might marry one day, who knows?" He picked up his glass and put it to his lips. Alida found herself dwelling on the possibility of his marrying and bringing his bride here, to Coral Cay...to the house he was intending to build...in her favourite place. Something sharp and hurtful seemed to be embedded in her heart, and a depression swept over her mind. No longer was the immediate scene bright and gay; she saw only a blur of lights when she glanced out to where the illuminations of the grounds created a delightful panorama of colour on fountains and flowers and lush tropical foliage. The lagoon was merely a dark pool, the reef a line of water faintly silvered by the moon. Darius seemed suddenly to guess at the change in her and he spoke quickly, assuring her again that the house he would build would not in any way destroy the beauty of Clearwater Cove.

She shook her head as he stopped.

"It wasn't that," she quavered.

"No? What was it, then?" he asked, his eyes uncomfortably searching as they stared into hers.

She sipped her drink, averting her face, wishing that Vance would return and join them.

"I felt depressed—about the house you're going to build."

"The house? Is that the only reason you were depressed?"

"Of course. What other reason could there be?" Fear that he had guessed at her feelings sharpened her voice unintentionally. A twisted smile touched Darius's mouth and lingered there a moment.

"None," he answered, "none at all."

Vance came hurriedly, full of apologies for leaving them, but said that this particular friend had turned up unexpectedly. He had been very ill—at death's door in fact—and the doctor had advised a complete change of surroundings.

"He decided on the Bahamas," Vance continued, taking possession of the chair he had left, "because he knew that my parents had a house, here, on Coral Cay. But he's become shy and reserved and he absolutely refuses to come and join us, either now, for drinks, or for dinner." Vance looked troubled and to Alida's astonishment she heard herself say,

"Do you want to keep him company, Vance? If you do, it's all right. Darius and I can dine alone...." Her voice trailed; she glanced at Darius from under her lashes, interested in his reaction. His face, lean and brown, was impassive as he said,

"Yes, it'll be quite all right with us if you want to dine with your friend."

"You're sure?"

"Of course."

"Well, thanks a lot. I'll see you home, though—"

"I'll walk home with Alida," interrupted Darius quietly and with a note of authority in his voice. "We'll probably be late, dancing."

Vance went off and Alida turned to the man she had thought she would hate till her dying day.

"You're sure—that you—you want to dine alone with me?" There was a touch of diffidence in her tone that brought a smile to his lips. She caught her breath. Had he always been as handsome as this! But no; in his youth he had lacked entirely the finely-drawn lines that full maturity had brought, the extra firmness of the mouth and jaw, the depths to his eyes.

"I shall be very happy to dine alone with you, Alida," he answered, and there was no mistaking the sincerity of his words. Life seemed suddenly to flow into her, warm and beautiful...and a new and tender emotion fluttered from dormancy to birth in her heart. Her eyes shone, drawing his whole attention in profound and silent interest as the glow was reflected in her expression, in the peerlessly moulded features, in the softly-parted lips that quivered like a child's. He said, for no apparent reason at all, "How young you are, Alida...how very young...."

Dining alone with him proved to be a most happy experience. He was the perfect companion, chatting during the courses and dancing in between. They sat in a window alcove all by themselves, eating Bahamian food which to Alida had never tasted quite so delicious— baked crabs and conch salad washed down with wine, rum-raisin ice cream with a thin slice of coconut tart, then an assortment of tropical fruits before the coffee and liqueurs and tiny bon-bons brought to the table in a silver bonbonière. There were candles on the table, and flowers in a silver vase. The view was to the marina, but nearer at hand were a dozen delightful glimpses—the fronds of a graceful coconut palm on the terrace flirting with the purple, star-flecked sky, the dancers who had strayed on to the patio where gay dresses caught the light and faces were happy, the colourful effect of lamps in the trees spraying crotons and hibiscus and oleanders with light. On the beach a dog ran in front of its master, then splashed into the lagoon.

"You're very quiet, Alida." Darius's voice brought a swift smile to her lips.

"I'm enjoying it all so much," she said. "Isn't this a wonderful part of the world?"

"Very." A small pause and then, "But you loved Cyprus once."

Fleetingly a shadow crossed her face.

"Once, yes, but on looking back, Darius, I can see, more than ever, how much I missed in life."

"And you also missed falling in love, didn't you?"

Something in the way he said that made her ask curiously, "Do you still think that falling in love is just for women?—that for men it's silly and sentimental?"

"Did I say that?" he enquired with a hint of amusement. "I probably did." Another pause before he added, "No, Alida, I do not think that falling in love is just for women."

Her heart caught, then seemed to turn a somersault as again she was asking herself if he liked her. Was it possible that he would fall in love with her after all this time? She thought of her mother, and Roger, and instantly shied away from the idea that had come to her, the idea that she and Darius could fall in love and marry. No, it must not happen! Such an eventuality would only bring unhappiness to the people who had cared for her and nurtured her through those dark days and months when she had been so ill, carrying a child she did not want and whose father she hated above anyone she had ever known.

"Let's dance, my dear." Darius was on his feet; she felt her body swung against his, knew the pleasure of his nearness, the touch of his hand, the smell of body lotion or after-shave that reminded her of the cool clean hills of Cyprus when the winds of spring brought down the scent of pines from the higher places on the mountains. He said to her after a while, "Have you never had anyone else, Alida?—never had an affair?"

She shook her head and looked up at him, a tinge of soft colour rising enchantingly in her cheeks.

"No, Darius, there's never been anyone else." She felt happy that she could say this truthfully, but wondered as she spoke if he had had affairs. He certainly had pillow-friends before his marriage and she supposed he must have had the same sort of friends since. After all, he was a Greek Cypriot and it was an undisputed fact that the Greeks were one of the world's most amorous peoples.

"This man, Vance," he said, "isn't he a special friend?"

"Special, yes, but not in that way."

Darius guided her towards the terrace, where the lights were low and the strains of an old island song came ringing through from the calypso group in the main ballroom.

"Not in that way," he repeated after a pause. "Aren't you concerned about marriage, Alida?"

"I think I told you that I haven't yet fallen in love." Her voice trailed almost to silence, because she was no longer sure that she had not yet fallen in love.

"He'll be a lucky man who wins your heart," he stated unexpectedly, and she glanced up into his face again. An odd sensation quivered at her heart, warm and exciting and yet indefinable.

"That's a strange thing coming from you," she murmured.

"I expect you do find it strange. It's true, nevertheless."

"A compliment. . . ."

"It was meant as one." He was guiding her farther away from the restaurant, guiding her to the far side of the terrace and there he stopped and stared down into her lovely face, his hands almost spanning her waist.

Every nerve was quivering with something akin to ecstasy; she was filled with a new yearning, a desire that was no more than a dream, nebulous, illusively tantalising. No words were spoken and yet Alida found herself on the beach. Darius pushed her gently on to a boulder of coral and before she realised what was happening he had bent on one knee and was taking off her sandals.

"Walk barefoot," he recommended. "It's delightful. The sand is so soft, like the finest powder."

"I know. . . I've done it many times. . . ." His hand came to hers and she was assisted to her feet. Amazed, she glanced down to see him carrying her sandals in his hand. For Darius to demean himself this way! Never would it have occurred in Cyprus, where few men even thought of carrying a heavy shopping bag or opening a door for their wives. She said, a trifle hesitantly,

"You've become very Westernised, Darius."

"I hope the change in me is for the best."

"Don't be humble—!" The words were out before she could stop them. She hated humility in a man as much as she hated undue arrogance. There was a happy medium, she thought.

"I'm not humble, Alida," he said swiftly and a little angrily. "But I have learned a great deal during the past eight years. I hope I'm a better man for those years."

Silly, but these words brought tears starting to her eyes and she stopped and sought a handkerchief. Darius stared as she produced one and wiped the moisture away. But he made no comment and they walked on again, along the deserted waterfront where the only sounds were the murmur of the breeze rustling the palms and the eternal surf breaking over the reef into the lagoon. Darius began to talk about his house and Alida found herself listening, enthralled, as he told her what it would eventually be like.

It was to be on the rise above the cove, and would therefore have one of the finest views in the Bahamas. It was to be built in the style of an old plantation house, built of coral limestone that would soon weather to a mellowed golden ochre.

"Like the ancient buildings at Olympia," he added with one of his rare smiles. "But you haven't seen them, I suppose?"

"No, we've not travelled in Greece at all."

"It's a wonderful country. You must go some time."

Was it only her imagination, wondered Alida, or had there really been a note of longing. . . as if he were wishing that he could have taken her to Greece?

"Tell me more about your house," she invited eagerly. "How big will it be?"

He glanced down at her, an odd expression on his face.

"You don't seem angry any more that I'm building at Clearwater Cove."

Alida walked on in silence for a moment, thinking about what he had said while at the same time enjoying the delicious sensation of powder-soft sand between her toes. It was like walking on a feather bed, she thought.

"No," she murmured at last, "I'm not angry—I haven't any right to be angry. The land's yours and you have every right to do what you like with it."

"As I said, I shall not spoil it."

"I'm sure now that you won't, Darius."

"Thank you for your faith in me." His voice was low, accented, and there was a smile on his lips as he added, "I'll not fail you...."

The way his voice trailed gave Alida the idea that, had he continued, he would have added, "...this time."

Emotion filled her; she wanted him to take her hand...to take her in his arms....

What folly was this! Swiftly she spoke, asking him again how big his house was going to be.

"I want four or five bedrooms, a study, and the usual entertaining rooms." He went on to say he intended having a swimming-pool surrounded by flowers and trees, with a sun-terrace at one end. "It'll be modern inside, yet from the outside it'll have the aura of a small manor house, and the lure of a tropical hide-away." He paused, but Alida said nothing; she was reflecting on the dramatic, almost unbelievable transformation that had taken place in his character, for at one time he would never have troubled to create something of such rare beauty as this house he was planning here, at Coral Cay. "I want the usual patios and I've already consulted one of the best landscape gardeners in Miami. The gardens will be made at the same time as the house is being built." He had slowed his pace and they were walking very slowly, away from the hotel lights, into the darker places of the beach. Alida fell to wondering what her mother would say were she to know what her daughter was doing at this moment. Roger, too, would be staggered, and exceedingly upset. Her behaviour was tantamount to letting them down, and suddenly Alida felt ashamed and her instinct was to turn and run from this man walking beside her, the man who had caused such an upheaval in three lives. But she did not run from him; she could not. Her decision stemmed not only from her own desire to be with him but also from the conviction that he would be dreadfully hurt.

And she knew she could never deliberately hurt him.

"Your house seems rather large for one person." She spoke at last, breaking the silence, aware that she just had to say something—anything, in order to divert her mind from her own feeling of guilt, and disloyalty to her parents.

"I did say that I might get married one day." Darius stopped and faced her; she looked up, an ethereal loveliness about her in the moon's silver glow. Darius's features were masked over with an inscrutable stillness that baffled her. What was he thinking? Had he a girl in mind already—the girl who would become his wife, and share the lovely house that was to be built at Clearwater Cove... *her* favourite place on the whole island?

Alida knew a terrible feeling of dejection. She could not live here if Darius brought his bride to Coral Cay.... Surely there was only one reason why she could not stay.... She flung the thought from her. She must not fall in love with him—she must not!

"Let's go back," she said, holding out her hand for her sandals. "I want to go back."

"Yes, of course, but don't put your shoes on yet—" He glanced down at her feet, just showing beneath the long blue skirt she wore. And then his eyes were on her face again, eyes that still held an unfathomable expression in their depths. And without giving her the chance to evade him, he bent his head and kissed her gently on the lips.

CHAPTER EIGHT

MARCELLE sat on the lawn glancing over a newspaper. Alida stood at the window of her bedroom, watching her, a brooding expression on her face. Marcelle had been here for over a week, and although her manner with her cousin was charming and friendly, Alida knew for sure that it was only a veneer and that Marcelle disliked her intensely. Roger had reached the same conclusion and several times he had remarked that he ought to have put his foot down and told Margaret that she was not to come. Marcelle had originally planned to come over for a fortnight, but she was now talking of staying for an extra week.

The decision had come after she had met Darius, reflected Alida, a sudden dryness affecting her throat, causing a little ache to settle there.

"Where are you, darling?" Margaret's silvery voice brought Alida away from the window, an invitation to enter on her lips.

"I'm here; come in, Mother."

Margaret came in and stood for a while looking her over.

"You're very attractive today, love,," she said. "That dress suits you. I told you you should wear green more often. You look so cool and fresh." She sauntered over to the window-seat and took possession of it, her eyes going naturally to the girl on the lawn. "I wish Marcelle would take herself off for an hour or so," she said with a frown. "She's always hanging about—" Margaret broke off and shrugged her shoulders. "I suppose she's come here to relax, and it's not unreasonable for her to do so. But Roger's here for a couple of weeks and he just can't stand her."

"Nor can I," said Alida, but silently. Aloud she agreed with her mother that it was not unreasonable for Marcelle to relax, to sit and enjoy the sunshine and fresh air.

"Roger says we're all going to the Fair Dawning tonight for dinner and the cabaret." A small pause and then, hesitantly, "Darius will be there, Mother, and Vance of course. Vance will ask Darius to join us. I hope you don't mind?"

Margaret's forehead was marred by a frown.

"This isn't the first time I've been forced to endure his company," she almost snapped. "And you, Alida— your attitude towards him amazes me. A week ago, when we dined at the Fair Dawning I was staggered to find that you and he were on such friendly terms! Roger, too, was shocked—but we told you all this when we came home, so you know how strongly we disapprove of the friendliness you show towards him. Why, after what you went through during that pregnancy, I'd have thought you'd rather kill the man than accept him as a friend! Besides, look what he's intending to do here. Most of the residents will have to look elsewhere if they want peace—"

"He's changed, Mother," interrupted Alida. "As for what he's going to do—well, he hasn't made a start on the hotel yet, has he?"

"What do you mean?" demanded her mother, her interest caught. "Has he had second thoughts about the project?"

"I don't know," replied Alida thoughtfully. "He's been asking me about the people who live here. He's met the Graysons and knows they had planned to retire here. He knows they haven't a great deal of money and couldn't really afford to sell up and move to another island. He also knows that anyone selling their house will lose money on it because of this building project and the influx of tourists that will result from it." She paused a moment, reflecting on Darius's interest in other of the residents. There were the Philpots who had a dear little place which had been a small clapboard house sold to them by one of the natives. They had done it up delightfully, but cheaply, because they had only limited means. They had retired only six months ago, believing they would end their days in peace on the little cay they had chosen from over two hundred islands. "He's been all around, and had a look at the village where the natives live. He said he thought it was quaint and ought never to be changed. He said the charm and friendliness of the people were even more noticeable than those of the Cypriots."

"He did? Well, he's improved by the sound of things!"

"There's a great difference in him, Mother. But you must have noticed it for yourself?"

"I've not seen him much apart from that occasion last week. We bumped into one another in one of the shops the other day, but civilities were all that passed between us. I dislike the man intensely and always shall! And if you want to please me and Roger you'll have nothing more to do with him!"

Alida swallowed. She had freely admitted to herself that she was in love with her ex-husband. How it had come about was a complete mystery to her, since by everything that was logical he was the last man on earth she should have fallen in love with.

"I have a feeling he won't build that hotel," she murmured at length, deciding there was no comment she could make on what her mother had just said.

"He'll lose a lot of money."

Alida nodded. She had already considered this.

"I know. And he's a businessman, but...." She lapsed into a pensive silence. "I do feel, instinctively, that he's not at all sure that he wants to carry on with the hotel and shopping plaza."

"And what about the house at Clearwater Cove? That's already started and getting well under way. He can hardly change his mind about that, can he?"

"He'd never change his mind. He's very keen about it." And so was she herself, thought Alida, for Darius had shown her the plans and the villa was going to be the most beautiful one on the entire island—more beautiful even than Mangrove Lodge. Marcelle had been there when Darius brought out the plans again, for Alida to see an addition he had made; it was an extra room overlooking a special spot that Alida had described as a fairy glade.

"I adore it!" she had exclaimed enthusiastically when, one afternoon, Darius had taken her down to the cove to see how the villa was progressing. "What a pity you haven't included a room that has it for its main view. But don't build over it, or in it, will you, Darius? I mean, a summerhouse or anything like that?"

"I promise, my dear," he had returned with one of his rare smiles. "I did say that I'd not spoil this lovely place which you think so much about, and I meant it."

Then, a few days later, had come the additional room. . . .

Marcelle had shown an interest out of all proportion, asking Darius to take her to the house so that she could have a look at what had already been done. As it happened, Alida had an appointment at the hairdresser's, so Marcelle went alone to Clearwater Cove with Darius. When she came back she was strangely quiet, but she did tell Alida that she and Darius had got along like a house on fire.

"He's terrific!" she had exclaimed. "And how incredible that you and he should meet again here, when you knew each other in Cyprus."

"I can't believe," mused Margaret, breaking into Alida's reverie, "that Darius will live there alone. I think I agree with Roger that he's building to sell."

Alida said nothing. Her mind was chaotic at times and this was one of those times. She had not been able to fathom Darius's attitude towards her, for it did seem that he liked her very much indeed, that he wanted to be friends with her. . . friends. . . and perhaps more? Yes, she mused, that was a question and not a statement in her mind, since he had made no real approach and it was only by putting her own construction on things he said, and on little gestures of attentiveness, that she had gained the impression that he might—just might—be falling in love with her. Yet what was to be the outcome if he did fall in love with her? Did she want to marry him after that unforgettable experience all those years ago? But he was a changed man; she knew instinctively that he would never again hurt her, or adopt that arrogant manner with her. There were other problems, though, major ones. She had to think of Roger, and of her mother, both of whom would be appalled at the idea of a marriage between Darius and their daughter. It would mean an estrangement, and that was something which Alida was not willing to let happen.

"He might get married," said Alida dully as the little cough her mother gave reminded her that she was waiting for some comment. "I don't believe he's building to sell."

"Married?" repeated Margaret with a lift of her brows. "God help the poor girl who's foolish enough to marry a man like that!"

Alida was in a long dress of white embroidered cotton; it made an alluring contrast to her honey-bronzed skin and gleaming dark hair. She wore gold earrings with a matching bracelet and necklace; her sandals were white, with pink toenails peeping through the lacy straps which were plaited intricately at the front.

Marcelle was more sophisticated in a slinky gown of black satin with a slit that went up the right side almost to the waist. Roger glanced at it with disgust, while Margaret, as soon as she had the chance, said to her daughter,

"Imagine wearing that here! It's more suited to the Ritz, or some other plush hotel in London. Why doesn't she look around and see what other people are wearing?"

"It suits her, Mother."

"You think so?"

"Yes—it's *her*, if you know what I mean?"

Margaret said nothing. In any case, Roger was there, ready to take them to the hotel.

Aperitifs were served in the old slave kitchen and both Darius and Vance were already there. Alida looked at him, saw his dark eyes wander appreciatively over her lovely form. She saw him swallow, as if getting rid of a blockage in his throat, noticed the swift pulsation of a nerve at the side of his neck.

He rose immediately, as did Vance, then the drinks were brought. Marcelle, surveying Darius from beneath thickly-mascaraed lashes, murmured in a husky tone,

"It's been so nice to meet you again, Darius. Are you here, at the hotel, permanently?"

"Not permanently, no," he returned suavely. "But I shall be here a good deal, until my house is ready, that is." His glance strayed to Alida and an inscrutable smile came to his lips. She coloured daintily, and lowered her head. No one must guess! Least of all her parents. She sensed that Marcelle's eyes were upon her, and Vance's too.

"It's too beautiful to live in all by yourself," purred Marcelle. "You'll have to get married, I think."

"Perhaps I will," returned Darius coolly, leaning forward to take up his glass from the table in front of him. "It all depends."

"Depends?" echoed Marcelle persistently.

"On whether anyone will have me." His eyes went again to Alida.

Roger broke in, abruptly, his tones short and crisp.

"Will you pass me one of those menus, Vance?"

It was given to him, and a waiter brought some more. There followed a discussion on the food as each said what they would have. Marcelle seemed fascinated by the mention of such gourmet fare as veal Milanese that was as light as a feather, fettucini Alfredo that brought a sigh from Vance, shrimp tempura and pressed duck, rack of lamb and thick steaks and many other exotic delicacies. Darius ordered steak and Alida the same. Marcelle said she would try the pressed duck.

The table was in the window and Marcelle somehow managed to sit opposite to Darius. Alida was to one side, with Margaret between her and Darius. Marcelle talked a great deal, mainly to Darius, and it was soon plain that she was attempting to gain his interest. However, it was with Alida that he danced first, and he told her that she looked especially charming in her white dress.

"You look especially charming, too, when you blush like that," he added, smiling down into her face.

She said nothing, her thoughts muddled and a little pang of despair in her heart. She was sure that Darius was well on the way to falling in love with her, and yet there could be no future for them even though she knew she could return his love.

Later she watched Marcelle dancing with him, and as she caught the look of unfriendliness in her glance Alida's swift-winged thoughts brought back with profound clarity that day when she had fainted in Marcelle's presence. Alida could not explain why this scene should present itself at this time, or why she should experience a strange unfathomable sense of foreboding, of danger....

"The phone's ringing. Shall I answer it?" Marcelle was at the french window, Alida sitting on the lawn.

"Yes, but I expect it's for Roger."

A moment or two later Marcelle was back again, her eyes narrowed, her mouth compressed.

"It's Darius—for you," she almost snapped. "I offered to take a message, but he said no, he wanted to speak to you." She came forward, her svelte figure clad in a pair of shorts and a brief suntop. She had acquired a tan, and as she passed her on the verandah Alida thought she had never seen a girl as attractive as her cousin. She wondered why she had never married, then recalled Aunt Lucie saying that Marcelle preferred the dark, foreign type of man. Yet she had wanted David, wanted him so badly that she had hated Alida because he had been interested in her.

"Hello, Alida." Darius's voice was quiet, accented. "I wondered if you would care to dine with me this evening?"

Her heart jerked. She and Darius had never dined alone since that night when Vance's friend had turned up and Vance had joined him for the meal, leaving Alida and Darius together. It had been wonderful, she recalled, and although she knew she should refuse his invitation, she found herself saying,

"I'd love to, Darius. What time do you want me to be ready?"

"Around eight. I'll call for you—"

"Oh—er—I'll meet you there, at the hotel."

A small silence followed; Alida could almost see the dry expression on his face when presently he said,

"Your mother and stepfather don't approve of me, is that it?"

She was pained, and speech threatened to become difficult. But she managed to sound casual as she said it was just as easy to meet him at the hotel.

"I shall enjoy the stroll in the cool evening air," she added, still in the same voice of casual friendliness.

"I shall come for you all the same," he said firmly. "I too shall enjoy the stroll."

She had to leave it at that, but there was an uneasy look on her face as she came away from the phone and Marcelle, standing sufficiently close for her to have heard what Alida was saying, examined her face intently, noticing the way she bit her lip, and the troubled expression in her eyes.

"Something the matter?" she asked smoothly. "You look worried, to say the least."

Alida started involuntarily; she had not realised that her expression was so revealing.

"Nothing's the matter, Marcelle." She had to force friendliness into her voice and a smile to her lips.

"Darius is taking you out this evening?"

"Yes, he is."

Marcelle's lashes came down, hiding her expression.

"I still think it's incredible that you and he should become acquainted again here. Darius is a long way from Cyprus."

"He's here because he's an investor in land," replied Alida, ignoring the second sentence. "People come from all over the world to the Bahamas to invest in land."

Marcelle looked at her in silence for a moment. Alida desired only to get away and opened her mouth to excuse herself, but her cousin was before her.

"It would appear that Darius is rather fond of you."

Alida shrugged, feigning indifference.

"Perhaps. I don't know."

"Aunt Margaret and Uncle Roger don't appear to like him very much."

Alida made no answer; her temper was rising, but she contrived to keep it under control. Marcelle spoke again, softly, her eyes fixed on her cousin's face.

"I wonder why they don't like him."

"He's intending to build here. None of us want building." Alida was frowning; she felt she should not be obliged to talk like this, but Marcelle continued to be persistent.

"Do you like him?" she enquired disconcertingly after a while.

"I don't dislike him," returned Alida evasively.

"Are you in love with him?"

Alida stared, dumbfounded by the forthrightness of the question.

"What a thing to ask!" she snapped when eventually words came to her. "Mind your own business, Marcelle!"

The older girl smiled rather vacantly and shrugged.

"I was only thinking," she murmured in a velvet-smooth voice, "that the Greeks are reputed to avoid like the plague any female who's had an—er—affair with another man. I'm talking about marriage, of course," she added swiftly. "They enjoy their friendships with this kind of girl, but marriage—well they look for a virgin when they want a wife."

Every nerve in Alida's body quivered. It was clear that her cousin knew she had had a baby.

"I don't quite know what this all about, Marcelle," she managed at last, feigning bewilderment, "but you're—"

"Why," interrupted Marcelle softly, "did Aunt Margaret marry in a hurry and rush you out of England?" There was no mistaking the measured import of her words or the significance of the glance she darted at Alida's figure.

"Why don't you ask her?" Sheer fury brought the response. "Yes, Marcelle, ask her! After all, it's her business—and Uncle Roger's, not mine!"

Amusement, and a sort of triumph, looked out of Marcelle's cold eyes.

"Would Aunt Margaret tell me the truth?" she drawled. "I very much doubt it." She paused a moment as if not quite sure how to frame her next words. "Aunt Margaret said you decided to come away from Cyprus because your father was arranging a marriage for you. I rather think, Alida, that it was for an altogether different reason that you ran away from your father. You were terrified, weren't you, because you'd. . . been having an affair and you'd got yourself—"

"Shut up!" broke in Alida fiercely. "Mind your own business! How dare you make insinuations about me—about my character! You're our guest! You ought to be ashamed of yourself!"

"What on earth's going on?" Margaret's voice behind them caused both girls to swing round. "Are you two quarrelling?"

"Oh, no, Aunt Margaret," answered Marcelle with a swift smile, "just having a discussion. If you'll excuse me—I want to have a swim. See you later!"

"Well," said Margaret, watching the girl's disappearing back, "what's the matter with her, I'd like to know?"

"She knows I've had a baby."

"Knows?" Margaret's eyes darkened with a hint of fear. "How can she?"

Alida went on to explain the scene when she had fainted, saying that she had had an idea that Marcelle was suspicious regarding her condition.

"The bitch. . . ." Margaret was thoughtful, her lips compressed. "Even if she'd guessed, she couldn't have said anything."

"No, she hasn't actually said it, Mother, but it's plain that she knows."

"She can't know for certain. It's impossible. Your child was born in Miami, and she's never been there."

"No, I agree with you that she can't be absolutely

sure, but—'' Alida gave a deep sigh and added, ''She *does* know, Mother, there's no doubt in my mind about that. She was on the point of actually saying it when I interrupted her. I was so angry.'' Alida paused a moment, then continued by telling Margaret that Marcelle had asked why she and Roger had married in such haste and taken her, Alida, out of England. ''She said I'd left Cyprus because I'd been having an affair and was terrified of my father. She was about to say I'd got myself in the family way, but it was then that I interrupted her. ...'' Alida's voice faded into silence, not because of the gasp of disbelief that issued from her mother's lips, but because a sound from the room behind had caught her ears. Marcelle had said she was going for a swim, and subconsciously Alida had been expecting to see her, had been watching for her to appear on the only path that led from the lodge to Roger's private beach. But she had not appeared on the path. The two maids were both in the far garden, one putting washing on a line and the other picking vegetables. The gardeners were working outside. Alida could see them, as she could see the maids. Roger was out. Who, then, was in that room...?

''How did the conversation come to take that particular turn?'' Margaret wanted to know. ''I mean, what was the reason for her hinting that you'd had a baby?''

Alida hesitated. She could scarcely believe that her cousin was eavesdropping in that room, but she suggested that she and Margaret go out to the garden and talk there. Alida could not help but dwell on the possibility of Marcelle's overhearing what had already been said. Well, if she had been listening she knew everything— No, not everything. She did not know that the child had been legitimate, and that Darius was its father.

"Let's sit in one of the arbours," suggested Margaret, and they strolled towards the one that was shaded by several bougainvilleas tumbling over a trellis, their floral bracts of red, orange and magenta creating an artist's palette of colours as they mingled with the cylindrical crimson spikes of the red bottlebrush tree that hung just above, and the lotus flowers of the magnolia tree whose branches bent low over the entrance. Alida sat down, but her mother remained standing, her eyes on the reef and the sparkling water that curled over it spilling into the sun-drenched calmness of the lagoon.

Alida began to speak, choosing her words carefully because although she was forced to give her mother some sort of explanation as to what had led up to Marcelle's coming out with the imputation that her cousin had had a baby, she had no intention of revealing all that had been said regarding Darius, and Alida's attitude towards him. However, it was inevitable that the invitation to dine should be mentioned, and when she heard it Margaret's interest in her niece was over-ridden by her anger and indignation that Alida should have accepted the invitation.

"You ought not to have accepted, Alida!" she snapped.

"I wanted to accept, Mother." Alida's voice was low, apologetic, and if her mother's ear had been sympathetic it would have caught the faint note of pleading that was in itself a sign of despair, and of the ache that gnawed at her daughter's heart.

"You wanted to accept?" Ice-cold the tone, accusing the gaze. "What on earth has come over you?" she demanded. And when Alida made no answer she added, after an eternity of silence, "You must be fully aware, Alida, that both Roger and I are not happy at the idea that you're beginning to regard Darius as a friend. You seem to forget what he did to you.''

"He's changed, Mother, I've already said so.'' The distress in her voice was far more revealing than she realised and her mother said sharply,

"You're not beginning to regard him as *more* than a friend, I hope!''

Alida shook her head, and a sigh escaped her.

"I wouldn't do anything to hurt you and Roger,'' she quavered.

Margaret's eyes were perceptive.

"You like him, but you'll put our feelings before any desires of your own, is that it?''

"Yes,'' answered Alida flatly, "that is it.''

"I never believed you could ever forgive the man,'' Margaret said with disgust.

"He isn't the same man.''

"The same man, but older; more mature, I'll grant you that. But he's still a Greek, still has all the arrogance that makes them believe in their own superiority. And custom will still be strong within him.''

"You're wrong, Mother. He knows now that what he did to me was cruel and insensitive. And he's very Westernised—but surely you've noticed?''

"I don't want to notice! I want him to leave here!'' Fear again, but slight. "There are reasons why you must not cultivate the man, Alida.''

"Reasons? What reasons?'' Alida looked curiously at her mother, aware that her eyes were evasive. There was some mystery, she knew, but knew also that her mother would never reveal it to her. She was baffled, and somewhat frustrated at not being able to understand her mother's strange attitude whenever Darius's name was brought into the conversation.

"Reasons which need not trouble you," replied Margaret. And then, after a pause, "Are you really intending to dine with him?"

"If you don't mind, Mother?"

"I do mind, and you're aware of it! Roger will be upset, too."

Alida turned away with a sigh on her lips. Any future with Darius was merely a faraway dream, for she would never, never, hurt her parents. In any case, she had no real proof that her ex-husband was in love with her.

"I must keep my promise this time, Mother," she said at last. "But I won't go out with him again."

CHAPTER NINE

ALIDA was not to be kept waiting long to discover whether or not her cousin had overheard the conversation which had taken place between Margaret and herself. It was as Alida was getting dressed for the dinner with Darius that Marcelle knocked on her bedroom door and entered in response to Alida's invitation. Alida was before the long, gilt-framed mirror and she looked like a Rembrandt portrait, with the hidden source of light from a pelmet above the mirror playing dramatically on her hair and her face, while the long flowing evening gown she wore was thrown into shadow so that the slender perfection of the figure inside it became tantalisingly seductive, lost in the subtle folds of rose-purple organza and fine lace. Diamonds were at her throat and wrist—presents from her stepfather on her twenty-first birthday, and in her hand she held a silver-backed hairbrush.

Marcelle stood motionless by the door just inside the room. Her face was set, her lips tightly compressed as she gazed her fill at the girl whose exquisite, classical beauty had outshone hers right from the start. She would always be beautiful, thought Marcelle, even when she was old. Envy, fierce and invidious, swelled to immense proportions which threatened to consume every shred of her conscious thought. She had come merely to put a few subtle questions to her cousin, to the girl who was invited out by the most attractive and fascinating man Marcelle had ever met. But as she stood here all sanity seemed to dissolve in the great, uncontrollable surge of jealousy that enveloped her in its net. She said, coming farther into the lovely blue and ivory bedroom,

"What happened to the child, Alida? Did you have it adopted?"

Alida didn't move. She continued to stare into the mirror, meeting her cousin's glacier-cold eyes unflinchingly. Only the loss of colour in her cheeks gave any indication that she had been affected in any way by Marcelle's question.

"Child?" she repeated, lifting her head slightly in a gesture of haughty enquiry. "Perhaps you'll be a bit more explicit, Marcelle."

A harsh laugh broke like a rasp on Alida's sensitive ears and a slight shudder passed through her.

"I overheard you and Aunt Margaret talking. I knew you'd had a baby, though—and you were aware that I knew. Well, what did you do with it? Did you get rid of it by having it adopted, or is it in a home of some sort? Of course, it'll be about eight years old by now, and that millionaire stepfather of yours might have put it into some exclusive and outrageously expensive boarding-school."

At last Alida turned to face her.

"I thought you'd listened, Marcelle." The glance she gave her held all the disgust she felt for her cousin. "Aren't you ashamed of yourself? You're a guest in our house and you listen at doors to what we're saying!"

"I discovered what I wanted to discover—proof that you'd had a baby." The blue eyes were brittle as glass, the voice sneering and malignant. "You haven't answered my question," she added after a pause.

"My baby was born dead."

"Dead...?"

Alida swallowed. She had been so happy a few moments ago, but now there was a hollowness in her stomach, and her heartbeats were like little hammers in her chest.

"Please go, Marcelle." She stopped, swallowing again, "I have nothing to say to you."

"Maybe not, but I have something to say to you." Marcelle's narrowed gaze was unfathomable.

"Please leave me," begged Alida again. "I can't think why you've made it your business to pry into my affairs, or what you hope to gain by doing so. I don't want you here, in my room—in fact, I don't want you in the house—"

"That's plain speaking, if you like—!"

"You've asked for it, Marcelle. Needless to say you'll never be invited here again. I hope you won't stay that extra week, but will go at the end of the fortnight."

"You're telling me to go?"

"It's plain that I am. You and I could have been friends, but from the first you haven't liked me. We've nothing in common, so it's best that you keep to the original plan and have just the two weeks."

"I might," said her cousin with a sort of amused malice, "try for a job here...and stay indefinitely on Coral Cay."

Alida stared disbelievingly.

"You've got an excellent job at home!"

"The idea of my staying here doesn't appeal, eh? You might have competition with Darius and that wouldn't fit in with your ambition which, naturally, is to marry a man at least as wealthy as your stepfather."

"I'm not thinking of marrying anyone," Alida said

quietly, glancing at the clock and realising that she should have met Darius five minutes ago in the lane outside the villa gates. "I've no time to talk any more." Putting down the brush, she took up a perfume spray to use on her wrists. Marcelle watched, dark malevolence in her eyes.

"If it hadn't been for you," she spat out, "David would have asked me to marry him!"

"Me? But he was interested only in his boat and—"

"And you, you know it! He'd no time for me after you appeared on the scene!"

"I soon disappeared from the scene," Alida reminded her, picking up a velvet cape and flinging it carelessly over one shoulder. She picked up her evening bag and moved towards her cousin. "If you'll excuse me, Marcelle, I'm already late."

It seemed at first that Marcelle would not let her pass, but she evidently thought better of it and stepped aside. Alida was about to leave the room, but turned. "After you, Marcelle," she said curtly.

"You don't trust me," sneered her cousin, moving towards the door which was wide open.

"As a matter of fact," returned Alida frankly, "I don't. You've proved, by your deliberate eavesdropping, that you're not to be trusted."

"I wonder," drawled Marcelle as she followed Alida from the room, "what Darius will say when he knows you've had a child...."

"Are you going to tell him?" Alida marvelled at the unemotional serenity of her voice, for although there was something amusing in the idea of Marcelle's trying to turn Darius against her by telling him she had had a child, there was a much more serious aspect to it in that Alida was determined that Darius should never learn that his baby had died. It would cause him immeasurable pain, Alida knew, and she knew she'd do anything to prevent that.

"I might...just depends, Alida." Smooth the tone and carrying a subtle, cryptic inflection that was, in this moment of haste, almost lost on Alida—almost, but not quite. However, there was no time for questions and answers, so Alida slid past her cousin as they reached the hall and the next moment she was through the front door and hurrying along the drive towards the high wrought-iron gates at the end.

Alida's thoughts, though, were still on what had just happened. Marcelle was jealous, that was plain enough. She obviously hated the idea of Alida's going out to dine with Darius; Alida remembered that she had said he was terrific! Was she falling in love with him? According to Aunt Lucie he would be exactly the type preferred by Marcelle—tall, dark and foreign-looking....

It was a balmy tropical evening with silver moonlight kissing the lagoon and the reef and the dark sea beyond. Alida and Darius had dined on the terrace, eating delicious lobster and filet mignon with a Bahamian salad and then an exotic Italian dessert. They had watched limbo and fire dancers, had listened to calypso music and they had chatted too, and been happy. Darius seemed to have undergone yet another change, becoming less reserved and stern, and he had laughed more than usual. They were now wandering along the shore where palms waved against a deep purple sky, and he was talking about his house. He wanted Alida to look at it in the morning, to give her opinion about the gardens he was having planned, and the position of the tennis court in the palm grove; he wanted her to say if the fell-ing of a few trees would be an improvement to the view, or whether she thought they ought to stay. They were pines and coconut-palms, he said.

Alida's happiness suddenly evaporated. She had promised her mother that she would not go out with Darius again, and although visiting his house at Clearwater Cove was not exactly going out with him, it was in effect breaking the promise she had made. She tried to sound light and casual as she said,

"I'm rather busy tomorrow morning, Darius, so I won't be able to come. I'm sorry."

"Later in the day, then?" He was almost like an eager schoolboy, she thought, glancing up into his face and seeing the smile that hovered on his lips, the expectation in his eyes. How could she refuse him? The pain of doing so was excruciating because she knew instinctively that he would be hurt. She hesitated a long while but eventually heard herself say,

"Yes, later in the day, Darius—after lunch."

"Good. You see, my dear," he went on gently, "it's very important that *you* like what's being done there, at your favourite place." He had stopped; she put a hand to her heart as if to stop its wild uncontrolled beating. That she could feel like this about the man she had hated for so long! That she could be in this state of ecstasy owing to those last few words he had uttered. Ecstasy. . . . Yes, it was there, filling her heart and mind. And yet despair mingled paradoxically; and the invincible barrier of her parents' total disapproval of this man.

He bent his head and kissed her gently on the lips, then his arms came about her and she was drawn towards his hard body. She strained against him, wanting him, desiring his kisses and caresses even while the picture crossed her mental vision, fleetingly, of that morning so long ago when she had fled from him in terror and disgust.

"Alida dear," he murmured, his lips close to her cheek, "I've decided not to go ahead with the building of the hotel complex."

"You've—!" She drew away, her eyes agleam. "I had an idea that you were reconsidering! Oh, but it's wonderful news! Everyone will be so grateful!"

"I know it."

"You'll lose a lot of money," she reminded him, a shade of concern in her voice.

"No matter. There are far more important things in life." He drew her to him and kissed her unresisting lips. "Dear Alida, I hope you know what I mean by those words?"

A question which could have been a proposal of marriage. She made no answer, thinking of her parents, her promise to her mother. Darius made no attempt to hurry her and together they began to walk on, treading the powdered pink sand under a tropical sky caressed by starlight. The lagoon slumbered, invitingly still, and one or two people were swimming in the moonlight. From the hotel there drifted the rhythm of the Goombay beat— that unique throb of Bahamian drums. It was magic, witchery, and Alida found herself caught in it, captured in a web of exotic glamour. Darius's arm came around her waist; she felt his long lean fingers through the flimsy material of her dress, strong fingers, cool, caressing....

"I said, my dear, that you would know what I meant when I said just now that there are more important things in life than the making of money."

She looked up and nodded.

"You've decided not to build because—because of—me?"

"Mainly, yes, I couldn't hurt you, not again—not ever—'' He stopped and looked down into her tender, limpid eyes. "You know, don't you, Alida, that I would never hurt you again?"

"Yes, I know." Her heart was weeping for what might have been. The barrier loomed even larger, because not by any stretch of imagination could she see her parents favouring a marriage between Darius and herself.

"The house at Clearwater Cove.... Alida, my darling, will you come and share it with me? Will you be my wife?"

She shut her eyes tightly, but the tears that had been pricking the backs of them escaped slowly, and fell upon her petal-soft cheeks. Darius stared, with perception and with tenderness as well.

"Your mother, and your stepfather...they wouldn't approve of your marrying me." A statement, not a question. She nodded dumbly, then buried her face in the white linen of his jacket. It was cool and comforting, like the hand with which he stroked her temple. "They remember that scene, when a foolish, self-opinionated youth forced his arrogant way into your mother's home and demanded that her daughter be returned to him." A sigh followed his words and a silence ensued after that.

"I've told mother that you're a changed man," quavered Alida at last, "but she isn't interested."

"I cannot blame her," he admitted. "I am sure I'd feel the same if the positions were reversed."

"We should all learn to forgive and forget, Darius."

"You have forgiven me?"

She smiled at him, a lovely, tender smile like that of a child who loves and knows he is loved in return.

"Of course. I wouldn't be able to love you if I didn't, would I?"

At that she saw a hint of amusement in his dark eyes, but there were thankfulness and gratitude there as well.

"So you love me. I wondered when you would say it."

"I didn't mean to. Oh, dearest, we can't marry! There's such a gigantic barrier!"

"Love knows no barriers. I shall come tomorrow and see your parents. I want you, Alida, want you for my wife, my dear friend, and my lover. I shall have you!" For one fleeting moment he was the arrogant Greek pagan who had married her, his voice forceful, imperious, his manner loftily possessive. She thought: he will always have some of that in him, because superiority is inherent in him. But he would be gentle too, and infinitely tender.... Yes, if he married her, but there was no possibility.... Or was there? Perhaps her mother and Roger could be melted, could be convinced of the change in him. A sigh escaped her. Even if they did in the end agree to a marriage they would never be happy about it.

"Darius—dear Darius, it can't be. It's because of the past—"

"Which is far behind us now, my love," he interrupted gently. "We must live for the present, and for the future. Crying over the past, or harbouring grudges for what happened then, is wasteful of one's time, Alida." He paused, but she said nothing and for a few seconds he held her close to her heart, and his hand continued to caress her temple. "As I've said, I shall come tomorrow to Mangrove Lodge and see your mother and stepfather. I shall tell them I love you and want to marry you—"

"No, Darius," she cried swiftly and urgently. "Please don't come yet! I'll talk to them—to my step-father. He loves me and wants me to be happy, so he might listen and understand." She looked up at him with eyes dewy with tears. "Please let me do it my way," she begged, and he nodded then and held her quivering body to him, murmuring soothing, reassuring words as his lips came slowly and lovingly to hers.

No more was said as they strolled hand in hand back to the hotel. This was a time and place for quiet companionship, for the appreciation of nature's gifts—the star-spangled sky and the slumbering sea, the placid lagoon and the tall palms fringing it, the coral sand beneath their feet. . . .

Darius's hand enclosing hers was reassuring; she no longer felt the weight of hopelessness and despair because she believed what he had said, that love knows no barriers.

She talked to Roger over breakfast the following morning, noticing his deep frown gather and the expression that was anxious and yet unfathomable. But there was no reproof or strong objection in his manner. He admitted that he had expected something like this because he had seen the way she and Darius were with one another, had read significance into Darius's words when he had said he might marry. . . if anyone would have him.

"He looked straight at you, my dear. And you knew, I think, exactly what was in his mind."

"You don't seem angry, or upset, Father," she said, surprised.

"I'm not angry, love, but it would be far from the truth if I were to say I favoured the marriage. You went through hell in that one night, from what I gathered at the time. Have you seriously considered the step you're contemplating, Alida?''

She nodded, but there was confidence in her eyes, fearlessness in her voice as she replied,

''Yes, Father, I have. Darius is a changed man; the years away from Cyprus have been most profitable to him and he's grateful for it.''

Roger nodded understandingly.

''I remember saying that he might improve with age, and your mother said the same... your mother....'' The frown that had vanished came again, darker this time and more prolonged. ''She'll never be at ease with him, Alida—no, it's quite impossible that she could be!'' The change of tone was startling, and in addition little lines of grey began to creep up the sides of his mouth. ''No, dear, it won't work! You must give him up!''

She stared uncomprehendingly.

''Roger,'' she said after a thoughtful moment, ''there's something I don't understand, isn't there? Mother appeared to be actually afraid when I said Darius was here, on Coral Cay. It seemed to me that her manner had nothing to do with his *reason* for being here, but soley because he *was* here.'' She paused and waited, but her stepfather made no comment and she sensed that he was fruitlessly searching for words. ''There's a mystery, Father, I know it. To be quite honest,'' she went on decisively, ''I overheard Mother say to you, when you were walking in the garden with her, 'Supposing he should find out!' What did it mean? What was there for Darius to find out?''

Roger had given a slight start as he heard Margaret's anxious words repeated, but he soon recovered.

''It was nothing that could concern you, dear. Just a little anxiety of your mother's—trivial, really—''

"She mentioned something about someone living in Florida, which, Mother said, was near enough." She looked at him interrogatingly from the opposite side of the breakfast table, but he avoided her gaze. "It concerns me, I know it." Another pause and then, "Was it something to do with the divorce, Father—?" But she shook her head immediately and answered her own question, saying no, it could hardly be that since it had been done legally, through the English court. Roger carried on eating, as if he were deliberately intending not to answer any questions or to be drawn into a conversation that could prove embarrassing for him. He was stolid, different in attitude from ever before. Alida said after a while, "The only solution is to ask Mother what it's all about."

"No!" The one small word came involuntarily, and it was plain that it was regretted at once. Roger sounded irritable as he added, "Just you keep out of things that don't concern you, Alida. You'll gain nothing by probing and questioning, and troubling your mother. Remember that her only desire is for you to be happy."

"In that case," returned Alida slowly, "she'll have no objection to my marrying Darius." Her voice was firm and decisive. She wanted to marry Darius and it was her life that was involved. She felt at this moment that whether her mother objected or not she would follow the dictates of her own heart, would accept what was obviously her destiny.

"We'll see when she gets up. I'll have a long talk to her—" He stopped abruptly as the doors opened and Marcelle, clad in a beach-robe over shorts and a bikini-top, came into the room, a smile on her face that could only be described as artificial. She sauntered towards the table, saying brightly,

"Hullo—good morning! May I join you?"

Roger picked up his coffee cup and hurriedly drank its contents.

"By all means join Alida. I shall have to ask you to excuse me. I've work to do in my study." He rose as he spoke, catching Alida's reproving eye and ignoring its meaning. "I'll see you later, dear," he said finally to his stepdaughter, and the next moment the two girls were alone, Marcelle sitting in the chair just vacated by Roger.

"I have a feeling that Uncle Roger doesn't like me." Marcelle spoke with a hint of amusement which was accompanied by a careless shrug of her elegant shoulders.

"He's a busy man," was all Alida said to that. She knew she ought to be civil at least, with this detestable girl, but at the same time she did not see why she should endure her company when she desired only to get away from her. So she merely waited until one of the maids entered to see what Marcelle wanted for her breakfast, and then she got up from the table, saying casually, "I too, must leave you, Marcelle. I've things to do. Please excuse me."

"Of course, but I shall see you later. I've something important to say to you, Alida."

For a moment Alida stared at her, undecided as to whether to stay or not, because she knew instinctively that what Marcelle had to say had something to do with that cryptic note in her voice last evening when she, Alida, had not time to stay and discover what lay beneath it. However, she decided to leave and let her cousin come to her later; she was not in the mood at present for hearing something unpleasant.

She was on the beach when eventually Marcelle came to find her. The sky was clear, sun-filled, the lagoon smooth and shiny as glass. Several people were swimming, or lazily taking the sun on loungers or large beach-towels. Alida was on the private part, on a sunlounger with a book unopened on her lap. She glanced up as her cousin appeared, and despite her determination to remain calm she felt her heart give a little lurch, and her pulse quickened slightly.

"How very content you look!" There was a sneer in the older girl's voice as she sat down on a towel that lay on the sand. "You've been just about as lucky as any girl could be, haven't you?"

"If you mean that I'm lucky in my parents, then yes, I agree."

"Why are some of us so much more fortunate than others, I wonder?" The sneer had gone, replaced by envy that was tinged with self-pity. "Did you enjoy yourself with Darius last night?"

Alida turned to look at her.

"What have you to say to me, Marcelle? Please say it and then leave me. I've no wish to sit here bandying words with you that are meaningless."

Marcelle's eyes glinted like chipped ice. Alida saw her hands clench suddenly and wondered how anyone could work themselves into so great a fury within seconds. Her cousin seemed convulsed with rage.

"You're so damned conscious of your position, aren't you! The petted and pampered stepdaughter of one of Miami's richest men! And if that weren't all you've got yourself another millionaire into the bargain! Well, I've already said that the Greeks never marry a woman who's had an affair, and Darius doesn't strike me as a man who would overlook the fact that you've had a baby!" She stopped, white with anger, her hands still clenched. "I admit that it still rankles that you came between David and me—"

"I did no such thing!"

"He'd have—" Again she stopped, and waved a furious arm in the air. "David doesn't matter anymore! I hate him! But I'm determined to have my revenge on you, Alida! I'm going to offer you the choice of giving him up, or of having him give you up! Have it which way you prefer!"

"I take it," said Alida with an outward calm that gave no indication of the nerve-twisting tension within her, "that you're referring to Darius?"

"You know I am!"

"You're threatening to tell him that I've had a baby?"

"It's a weapon I shall use if necessary."

"Because you can't bear the thought of my marrying him?"

"You've got enough—more than enough! I hate you, Alida, I always have. The last time I came here you were just as smug, living it up on an island in the sun while I have to work in a stuffy office!" She turned away and Alida knew for sure that she was fighting tears of fury and self-pity. *How glad I am that I don't possess the gene for envy,* thought Alida. It was cankerous, soul-destroying, excruciatingly painful. She said quietly after a while,

"I've never been smug in my life, Marcelle."

"You're smug now! I believe Darius has proposed to you—it was evident that he was trying to please you when he built that extra room! It was evident the other night, at dinner, that it was you he had in mind when he said that perhaps he'd get married!"

Alida said nothing for a moment, for she was think-ing of the threat and feeling that, in the end, Darius would have to know about the child.

"I don't know what to say to you, Marcelle," she sighed at length. "If it's your intention to try to spoil my life by telling Darius that I've had a baby then I can't stop you. But I can assure you that it won't make any difference to his attitude towards marriage with me."

"What...?" Marcelle's eyes narrowed. "What ex-actly do you mean by that?"

"I'm not willing to explain," said Alida shortly and, getting up, she walked swiftly away towards the path leading up to the house.

Her mother and Roger were on the patio; they both looked up at Alida's approach and Roger rose from his chair, gesturing for her to take possession of it.

"Thank you, Father." She watched her mother's face; it was brooding, thoughtful, and there was a frown between her eyes. Roger brought another chair and sat down, and it was he who did the talking, saying that they were both disappointed at the idea of her fall-ing in love with her former husband, that he was not their idea of the man she ought to marry. On the other hand, Roger said that they both realised that she was her own mistress, and that if she made up her mind to marry him there was nothing that either of them could do. Alida interrupted at this point to say that she wanted their blessing, if that was at all possible.

"He really is a changed man," she told her mother. "You must know I'd never, never marry the Darius I once knew."

"Yes, we've thought about it," said Roger after giv-ing his wife the opportunity of commenting. "He must have changed considerably for you to have fallen in love with him.''

"Are you willing for me to marry him, then?" It seemed like a miracle! Yet she knew that even if they *had* objected she would have persevered, attempting to bring them round, for she knew without any doubt at all that she intended to marry her ex-husband.

"We've talked a long while, and reached the conclusion that we really have no alternative but to accept the situation." It was Margaret who spoke at last, her voice and her expression clearly indicative of the disappointment she was feeling at the idea of having Darius for a son-in-law. "However, there is one thing, Alida, that I would ask." She glanced at her husband, whose face, Alida noticed, was totally without expression. "I want you to promise that you'll never mention to Darius that you've had a baby. We feel that he's the kind of man who would want to know more about it—"

"Is there any reason why he shouldn't know?" asked Alida, diverted for the moment, and puzzled. She saw her mother's eyes dart again to her husband's face and something indefinable rippled along her spine.

"I—er—we feel that he'd be better off not knowing about the child."

Alida was still puzzled, but as under the present circumstances there was nothing to be gained by pursuing the matter she allowed it to drop. She herself would have given anything to spare Darius's feelings regarding the child, but Marcelle's threat precluded any possibility of this.

"I'm afraid, Mother, he'll have to be told. Marcelle overheard us talking and now she knows that I did have a baby. She's threatened to tell Darius about it unless I give him up."

Both her listeners stared, their expressions portraying complete bewilderment.

"What on earth are you talking about?" demanded Roger at last, and Alida went on to explain, repeating almost everything her cousin had said. Silence followed for several seconds, as the colour slowly left Margaret's face and strange unfathomable glances passed between her and Roger.

"You can't marry him," said Roger with a decisive shake of his head. "It's quite impossible!"

Alida blinked.

"Impossible? I don't understand? Just now you were both resigned—"

"We were," replied Margaret unsteadily, "but only if you promised not to tell him about the baby."

Bewilderedly her daughter shook her head.

"It doesn't make sense, Mother! I myself would prefer to keep silent about the child, simply because it would hurt Darius to know that—"

"You can't marry him!" snapped her stepfather, and there was a stony edge to his voice that Alida had never heard before. He was usually so gentle, so affectionate in his way of speaking. "It's out of the question! You must finish with him altogether! We shall move to Miami Beach, to our other house! Yes, that will be the most practical course to take. Mangrove Lodge will have to be sold, there's nothing else for it." He glanced at Margaret. She was shaking her head. Her face had gone grey; she looked positively ill, thought Alida.

"We'll have to tell her, Roger! There's no help for it! After all, I did it for her, so she can't condemn me!" Margaret's voice rose to a shrill crescendo, halted only by her husband's stern injunction to stop being hysterical.

"There isn't any need for her to know!" he added wrathfully, but of course it was plain to see that he was aware of the futility of trying to put his stepdaughter off now. After a long moment of silence she said, her eyes fixed on her mother's shrinking figure,

"What is it you have to tell me? And why do you mention the word condemn? How could I condemn you for anything?"

She had no idea what to expect, as she sat there, waiting for her mother to speak. Margaret's face was drawn and she actually looked her age as, with what was the greatest difficulty, she began to speak to Alida, slowly, haltingly, with many pauses between her sentences. She watched her daughter's hands come up to press convulsively against her throat, saw the colour drain entirely from her face as the blood left it, saw her shake her head disbelievingly, and her lips part as she tried to utter words that would not come.

"And now you know it all," Margaret ended. "I did it for you, and you alone."

"My...child...my baby...isn't dead...." The disjointed sentence came at last, issuing from lips frozen and stiff. "He—he's adopted...." Alida's mouth relaxed now, twisting this way and that as emotion writhed within her. "He belongs to—to someone else—Darius's son—and mine." She closed her eyes tightly, her mind becoming blurred, torpid because she did not *want* to think, to visualise her child—her eight-year-old son—calling someone else mother.

"Alida, my dear child...." Roger was the first to recover from the mental inertness that had been affecting them all. He rose and came over to his stepdaughter, slipping an arm about her shoulder. "When you've got over it you will accept that we did it for you. Yes, dear, I aided and abetted your mother because I felt it was kinder to let the child go than for you to be burdened with it for life. You'd have had to keep the name of the man you detested; you'd have had less chance of marrying well—"

"Please, Father, stop! I can't think!"

"Try to think, dear," he persisted. "Try to take in what I'm saying. You didn't want the child—"

"At the end I did," she broke in dully.

"Only at the end, but we didn't set much store by that. In any case, we believed we were doing the best for you, never thinking for one moment that Darius would ever cross our paths when we were so far away from his country. You'll see, love, that it's best for you to give him up, because if he ever found out that his son was alive, he'd be bound to demand his return."

"You couldn't blame him for that," said Alida in the same dull tone of voice. Darius, father of an eight-year-old son.... Of course he would demand his return!

"If he did demand his return," Roger went on, "it would be a terrible tragedy for your mother. You do see that, don't you?"

"She—she said the child was—was hers, so she was able to—to sign the papers for—for its adoption." The words were an effort, drawn out of her by some force she tried to control, for she did not want to say them. Her mother was a criminal. Yes, in the eyes of the law she had committed a crime.

"If Darius insisted on claiming his child it would all come out," Roger was saying. "Your mother could go to prison—"

"No, no!" Margaret glowered at her husband. "Don't say such things, Roger! In any case, you'd be in trouble as well—for aiding and abetting me! You'd be prosecuted along with me and we'd both be—be found guilty!''

A silence fell after this outburst and Alida tried to think, to conjure up a picture of her little boy—a fine boy, surely, because he was Darius's son. He'd be tall for his age, and dark, with fine strong limbs— Her thoughts broke there. How could they have said he was dead!

Roger was speaking, saying something about the removal to Miami Beach.

"There's no need for that," she told him flatly. She looked at them in turn, her eyes dull and lifeless. She knew their intentions had been good at the time of her baby's birth, and some vague insistence at the back of her mind told her she would forgive them one day. But for the present only the consequences of their act were filling her consciousness. She had lost Darius, and both he and she had lost their child.

"I can't marry Darius," she went on in a low voice. "As you say, Father, it's impossible, firstly because the child's birth can't be kept from him on account of Marcelle's threat, and secondly, even if no such threat existed, I could never carry this secret through years of marriage, not now that the knowledge has come to me that our child is alive and—and the s-son of—of someone else." Again she looked at them, her mouth twisting convulsively. "I'll—ask you about his—his home and—and parents some time, but for now—" She broke off and shook her head. "For now I don't w-want to know."

Darius, she thought, would leave Coral Cay—sell the house at Clearwater Cove—when she told him she was not marrying him, that she had thought about it and decided she was afraid to take the risk after what had happened before. Yes, he would leave, she was convinced of it, so there would be no need for Roger to arrange a move to his other house on Miami Beach.

"Alida dear...." It was Roger who spoke, and he would have taken her in his arms but she gestured him away.

"We did it for you," said Margaret, and there was a hint of indignation in her tone as if she resented the attitude her daughter was taking. Alida looked at her, remembering only that her mother had stated quite categorically that she could not be bothered with a child in the house at her age. But all Alida said was,

"Yes, I know you did it for me—you believed at the time that you were acting for the best." She turned then, and left them, her thoughts inevitably on her child, the little boy whose home was somewhere in Florida, who had parents that were not his natural ones....

She reached her room and as her thoughts switched to Darius her heart gave a great lurch. It was something she could not control because for a fleeting moment she could visualise his wrath if he should ever learn that his child had been adopted...and his wrath would be directed against her, simply because, in order to save her mother, she would have to say that she had signed the adoption papers that gave their child to someone else.

CHAPTER TEN

THE lovely site of the house at Clearwater Cove was not the setting for what Alida had to say, but she had promised to meet Darius there—to give her opinion on various aspects of the villa, she recalled bitterly—and she arrived early, fifteen minutes before time. The workmen were taking their afternoon break and the site was deserted. She glanced around, marvelling at the swiftness with which such good quality work had been done. But Darius had far more men on the job than was usual; it was plain that he wanted the building done in a hurry.

Tears stung her eyes as she wandered through the lovely grounds and saw how cleverly the original vegetation had been preserved. It was all for her... because this was her favourite place and she had not wanted it spoiled. The beach was there, so close, and already a delightful path had been made to it from the grounds of the villa, a path constructed of pearly-pink coral limestone in which she could see a delightful array of brachiopods and lamellibranchs and numerous other evidences of coral life long since turned to stone. The site for the tennis court was delightfully placed, for not only was it surrounded by swaying palm trees but there was a riot of mauve bougainvillea trailing along the border fence.

A sound made her turn; she saw Darius hurrying along, avoiding the builders' rubble, his long lithe frame clad in dark blue linen slacks and a snow-white short-sleeved shirt. How handsome and distinguished he looked! If only he had been like this when first they had met! If only they had been allowed to fall in love and marry because they both wanted to— She cut her thoughts since they were profitless, and forced a smile to her lips as Darius reached her and said,

"Have you been waiting long, dear? I'd meant to be here first so I could receive you as my guest. But," he added with a sudden smile, "you are not a guest, are you, my darling? You're my partner and my—"

"Darius—stop!" she cried, unable to let him continue. Her face was pale as she looked up at him, her eyes bright with unshed tears. "Please don't talk to me like that. I can't marry you," she whispered, and brushed a hand across her face because the tears had already begun to fall. "It just can't b-be. I'm not willing to take a chance, n-not after what happened before. It would be madness. So it's to be goodbye. That's what I came here for today, to say goodbye—once and f-for all!" She twisted her body and would have run from him, but his hand shot out and gripped her wrist. And as the movement would have caused her to overbalance he jerked her towards him and for a moment she felt the exquisite pain of contact, the thrill of his body against hers. His other hand beneath her chin forced her to meet his eyes, compelling eyes that narrowed with perception and then glinted with anger.

"You didn't do very well there, did you, Alida? Your parents are at the bottom of this, but your love for me will win! Do you suppose I shall part from you, just like that? My dear Alida, I might have changed, but I'm no spineless jellyfish! No one—no one, do you hear?—is going to come between us! We love each other; we've found what in my belief we would have found anyway, had we stayed married, simply because I would have fallen in love with you, madly in love, and you would have learned to love me—after you'd forgiven me, that is."

His voice had dropped from an angry, harsh note to one of quiet tenderness, and the hold on her wrist was now the gentle caress of a lover. Alida's tears blurred her vision and she saw only a dark shape above her, dark and severe. But as she blinked away the tears she saw the tenderness there, in his eyes and his mouth, softened by the half-smile that hovered there. "You were unconvincing just now, to say the least, my darling, but in any case your lovely eyes are telling me, even at this moment, all I want to know. We were meant for each other, but fate threw us together in circumstances that were shattering for you; and as a result many long years have been wasted. But no more shall be wasted," he continued seriously, "because as soon as this house is ready for my lovely bride I shall be carrying her over the threshold."

Alida tried several times to interrupt him but failed; his words were sweet to her ears even though she knew they had no real meaning simply because what he was saying could never materialise. She and he were doomed to separation for ever, because of a little boy who was living somewhere over the water, in Florida, a little boy who was theirs but who belonged to someone else.

"Darius, I—"

"Don't say anything else, my love. I shall see your parents this evening. I'll phone and make an appointment. They'll lift any objections once I have talked to them and convinced them that I adore you and can't live without you."

He drew her close and kissed her quivering lips, and

she did not draw away. She would take these few sweet moments, treasure them forever in the loneliness ahead, and when she got home she would write him a letter, telling him not to visit her parents as her decision had nothing to do with them. She was unwilling to marry him and her decision was final. Whether or not he would accept that and leave her alone was certainly a debatable point, but at the back of her mind was the idea of leaving Coral Cay for a while and living over at Miami Beach. Darius had no idea where Roger's other house was situated and she could only hope that he would not trouble to find her.

"Darling...." His lips were lightly touching hers, cool and clean, like the caress of the breeze coming over the lagoon to kiss the powder-soft shore. "You know, dearest, I can hardly believe you would let your parents influence you. There isn't anything else, is there?"

She shook her head at once, her heart leaping within her. If he should ever discover— But there was no chance of such a calamity. There was no one to tell him, not once she had given him up and left the island. Marcelle would be satisfied and therefore would keep the secret safe.

"No, Darius, there's nothing else."

He seemed to frown as if perplexed about something, but a moment later he was bringing her unresisting body into the haven of his embrace and his lips were tender as he took possession of hers. Bliss! She strained to him, her arms around his neck.

"My beloved, my own dear—" Without warning he broke off, pushing her gently from him. She stared, then spun round, her bewilderment turning to dismay as she looked into the malevolent face of her cousin.

"Marcelle! How long have you been there?"

Before she could answer Darius was speaking, greeting her politely. He always treated her in this way, because of course she was Alida's cousin and a guest in her home.

"You've come along to see how things are progressing?"

"Yes...." Marcelle's eyes left Alida's face to glance all around. Even at this stage it was easy to see that the villa was going to be very lovely, in its exotic and highly romantic setting on this secluded little corner of an island that was in itself a tropical paradise, a jewel of rare beauty in a necklace of other islands that dreamed beneath the clear Bahamian skies. "It's coming along...." She stopped as if she had run out of words. Alida, watching her closely, saw the fury in her eyes which seemed to mingle with sheer hatred as her gaze returned to her cousin's face. Alida was fully aware that the scene Marcelle had come upon just now had given her an entirely wrong impression, but although she was troubled it was not unduly so. Once away from here she would tell her cousin that she had given Darius up, that she was finished with him altogether.

"You like it?" Darius had moved as if he were about to show Marcelle around. "We're having a tennis court among those palms, and a swimming-pool over there, to one side of the little stream that comes down from the rocks—" He pointed and would have walked on, but Marcelle spoke, softly, invidiously, asking him why he had used the expression, "We're." "Because," he answered before Alida had time to stop him, "Alida and I are to be married."

Silence. Marcelle's mouth bent to a convulsive shape that caused a shudder to run along her cousin's spine, and her eyes opened wide like someone who has become possessed of a madness of some kind. Envy, terrible to see, was there in every line of her face. She seemed unable to articulate words for a moment, but eventually she said, her voice harsh, guttural even, like that of a jungle beast out for destruction,

"Married? But what a surprise!" A pause. Alida, suddenly alert and trembling, realised that there was not a second to spare. She opened her mouth to say something, anything! But Marcelle was before her, saying in the same soft and dangerous tone of voice, "You surprise me, Darius, because I didn't think that you Greeks ever married girls who had had affairs—who had had babies by other men!" The last words were spat out from the lips of a girl who had lost all sense of politeness or tact, who was carried on a tide of jealousy that deprived her entirely of rational thought, and swept her instead into a spate of malice meant to destroy for ever any happiness that Alida might have had. "Did she confess about the baby? Did she tell you how her mother and stepfather rushed her out of England so that none of us would know about it?" Her eyes swept over Darius with contempt. "Perhaps you're not so particular after all—most men aren't these days, I must admit—"

"When," interrupted Darius with quiet dignity, "did Alida have her baby?"

"Eight years ago—" Marcelle stopped abruptly, staring at him. "You're very calm about it. Don't you care?"

"Darius...." Alida found her voice at last, speaking through the dryness that affected her throat. "Don't listen to her. Please don't...."

Marcelle was laughing almost hysterically, but it was triumph that looked out of her eyes.

"He didn't know! Well, he knows now, doesn't he!" She turned to him again. "Will you marry her now, Darius—now that you know she's had a child?"

The contempt in his gaze as it swept over Marcelle's figure brought a flush to her cheeks, but she turned away with an arrogant flounce, her head in the air.

Alida stared at Darius, her mind in a torpor, for she could not collect her thoughts, was totally unable to picture the outcome of all this. If only she had talked to Marcelle before coming here; if only Marcelle had waited.... What was the use? What was done was done and all Alida wanted at this moment was to run away, a million miles away, and find peace.

His eyes were piercing when presently they met hers, but he was answering Marcelle's question, using that same tone of quiet dignity as he said,

"Yes, Marcelle, I will marry her now. You see," he added, transferring his gaze to her as she spun round at his words, "Alida's baby was mine. We were married in Cyprus when she was seventeen."

"Married...!" Marcelle's mouth gaped. "You were married to her once?"

"Kindly leaves us!" Darius flicked a hand towards the path. "Neither of us desires your company. Get off this site!"

"I—"

"Get off!" he rasped. "You're despicable!"

It seemed for a space that Marcelle would refuse to obey him, would ask some questions in the hope of satisfying her curiosity, but as Darius's expression conveyed the warning that if she did not get off the site he would physically assist her off, she paused only to throw her cousin a look of venomous hatred before striding away in the direction of the path which had been indicated to her.

A long silence followed her departure, but at last Alida heard her former husband say,

"Where is our child?"

Her mouth was dry, her lips stiff and parched. She wished the workmen would return, for she would feel safer.

"It was a boy," she managed at last, evading his question as she tried to gather her thoughts together... and some courage along with them.

"Was?" sharply and interrogatingly.

Strange that she should have forgotten that their son was alive, and well.

"He—he w-was adopted," she began.

"Adopted?" Disbelieving the voice, painful the hand that gripped her arm to bring her round again as she turned away from that fierce, accusing gaze. "You had him adopted—without consulting me?"

"He w-was mine," she faltered, flinching as his grip tightened. "At the—the t-time it seemed the best th-thing to do."

The silence that followed was filled with nerve-jolting tension.

"You didn't want him, is that it—because he was mine?"

She looked down at her feet, ashamed that she had repeated over and over again to her mother and to Roger that she did not want the child. But at the end... yes! She had wanted it with all the possessive instinct of motherhood, had looked forward to holding it in her arms, putting it to her breast, even though, at that time, she was little more than a child herself.

"At first, Darius, I didn't want him, no, because I'd had no part in—in making him, as we say, in Cyprus."

She paused, aware of her rising colour, aware that the grip on her arm had tightened yet again.

"At first?" he repeated harshly. "What about afterwards?"

She had made a slip! Only now did she realise it. In a sort of desperation she floundered mentally through several explanations before a feasible one presented itself to her.

"I'd already made arrangements with the new parents and I couldn't go back on my word."

"Liar!" he rasped. "A mother can always go back on her word in a case like that! You didn't want it, not at any time, did you—because it was my child! God, if only I'd known! My father died an unhappy man when he could have been told that—"

"What did I care about your father?" broke in Alida, managing to summon up a modicum of courage. "I wasn't a machine, bought to manufacture a child for his pleasure!"

"You were my wife, the mother of my unborn child!" He was so wildly furious that the flaw in that statement escaped him altogether. "Where is my child?" he thundered. "I shall consult a lawyer about getting it—"

"No!" she cried, twisting from him and beginning to run. "You can't!" she said over her shoulder. "You'll never find out where he is—never!" She was running swiftly, intent on getting home and informing her parents of what had transpired. They must be warned so that they would be prepared for the visit which Darius must undoubtedly pay them. He soon caught up with her, and he took her by the shoulders and shook her unmercifully, shook her till her heart and lungs seemed ready to burst. Tears sprang to her eyes. He was not changed—not one little bit! How could she have thought so? He was still a pagan, capable of torture when his unbridled wrath escaped control. She had had a narrow escape. Nothing—*nothing*—would induce her to marry him now, after this demonstration of his primitive brutality.

"Where is my child?" he demanded again when at last he held her from him, supporting her because she was swaying unsteadily on her feet. She looked into a face twisted with fury, into eyes that terrified her by the threat lying within their depths. If her mother should be prosecuted, and Roger too... Roger who was so well respected both here and in Miami. Oh, God, it must not happen! She must do something to prevent Darius from discovering the child's whereabouts.

"I shan't tell you! I had it adopted and it's nothing to do with you! It was mine—"

"And mine." His voice was quieter than before, but the determined inflection was still there. "You were not in a position to have it adopted without my consent. I did not give that consent and therefore the adoptive parents shall be forced to give me my son."

Alida looked at him in despair. He would show no mercy; he would not care about her mother, or Roger... and yet, why should he? From his point of view things looked entirely different. He had a son, an eight-year-old son whom he had never seen. He wanted his son, who was his heir also, and in all fairness Alida had to admit that his attitude was the most natural in the world. In fact, it would be most *un*natural if he had not been eager to gain custody of his child. However, there were many other aspects to the situation and all that filled Alida's mind was the urgency of getting home to warn her parents of Darius's impending visit, which was the result of Marcelle's malicious disclosure.

The men were filtering back to the site in twos and threes; now was her chance, she thought, and began to hasten away, her pace increasing to a run. Surely Darius would not be so undignified as to chase after her in full view of his workmen. What they might think of her mattered not at all, and as she reached the end of the main building she put on even more speed. As she had surmised, Darius followed at a more sedate pace, but a formidable one for all that. It was plain that he did not intend to give her much time alone with her parents before he himself put in an appearance.

Breathless when she entered the villa, she called to her mother, then called again, this time in a high-pitched, urgent voice, but there was no answer. Roger too was out, she realised as she ran from room to room.

"Where are they?" On the beach perhaps! She turned and raced along the path, wondering where her cousin was and feeling relieved that she too was not in the house.

There was no sign of any of them on the beach, but as she turned to go back she saw Vance in the distance. He waved and came along, leaping over the fence that separated Roger's private part of the shore from that along which he had been approaching. She waited in a fever of suspense and impatience for him to come up to her.

"Hello, coming in for a swim?" he asked cheerfully.

"No, I'm looking for my parents. Have you seen them about? It's terribly urgent!" Her voice broke in the middle and she realised she was very close to tears.

"What's the matter?" he began, but she interrupted him at once asking again if he had seen her parents.

"As a matter of fact I have seen them, about ten minutes ago, strolling along the beach—"

"In which direction?" she asked. "Will they have gone far?"

"That direction," he answered, thumbing towards the south. "I should think they'll have got a good way, yes."

"I must find them. I'll see you some other time—" And she was off like a flash in the direction he had indicated.

She failed to catch up with them and eventually made her way back to the villa. Her mother was on the patio, standing by the rail looking out to sea. Her stepfather was behind her...talking to Darius....

Alida's heart raced though her footsteps flagged. Too late! Her mother's face was grey and drawn as she turned to watch her daughter's approach. She said, as Alida reached her,

"He knows everything. Your lie was well-meant but useless. He'd soon have discovered that it was I who signed the papers—" She broke off and shrugged. "He's intending to get his son." Margaret looked at her and sighed. "He wants to marry you—he wants you both." Another pause and then, "He loves you, child, I'll not deny that. I'd never have believed that a man could change in the way he has—but there it is. However, he's not going to show any mercy, and who can condemn him for that?"

Alida was pale but her mother's face was now milky white, and her hands on the rail were clenched so tightly that the knuckles showed through the pale transparency of the skin.

Alida went past her and stood close to the two men, both of whom turned to look down at her. It was Roger who spoke, and to Alida's surprise his voice was quiet, resigned, without any sign of resentment or anger.

"It's a case of the truth will out," he sighed. "Darius has put his case forward and both your mother and I agree that is within his rights to try to demand custody of his son.''

''You want him too, my dear?'' This came gently from Darius as he reached for her hand and took it in his. ''My love. . .I've learned how you suffered, learned that you were close to death on more than one occasion.'' He looked deeply into her eyes, uncaring that there were witnesses to his humility. ''I beg your forgiveness, Alida, crave it, in fact. My only excuse is that of inexperience when I offered for you and married you against your will. I'd never learned a single lesson at that time about life and the way it should be lived; I knew nothing about love and companionship and the fact that women should be men's equals. But I've learned it all since, and if you'll have me you'll never regret it, never for one single moment in your life.''

She was weeping softly, her mind torpid again, for although she had listened intently to Darius, and taken in every word, she was still absorbed by the dire situation facing her mother and stepfather.

''I can't see my mother go to prison, Darius,'' she whispered, aware all at once that Margaret had gone and that Roger was edging away towards the door. ''Isn't there something that can be done?''

He shook his head and she saw a hardness enter his eyes.

''Your mother's resigned, darling, and so is Roger. I want our son, Alida, and so do you.''

She nodded her head, brushing a hand across her cheek to sweep away the tears.

''I'd love to have him, Darius—of course I would. But the cost—'' She looked at him pleadingly. ''There's some way, surely? Please think of some way to save my parents from prosecution.''

"It might not come to that if the adoptive parents can be persuaded to part with him without fuss."

"They won't," she cried shaking her head. "Would you part with a child you'd had since he was a baby—without fuss? No, they'll put up a fight, Darius, because they'll have come to love him; they consider him as their very own!" The tears came again as she pictured the heartbreak of her son's adoptive parents. "The court might not agree to our taking him from them," she suggested as this most logical idea came to her. "The authorities always think of the child's welfare before anyone else's."

He took her by the shoulders and looked down into her tear-filled eyes.

"You sound as if you don't want our child, Alida."

"I do want him—!" She shook her head bewilderedly. "I'm so confused, Darius. I want him *achingly*—but on the other hand there's going to be some terrible heartbreak over this."

"They'll get over it," returned Darius implacably.

"And the child—our son?"

"He's only eight; he too will get over it—quite soon, I should say. Children are like that."

Her mouth quivered and she closed her eyes tightly.

"What a muddle!" she whispered. "Oh, Darius, what will be the end of it all?"

"We'll be a united family, Alida," he told her seriously. "All these years we've been separated, but now fate has thrown us together, you and me first, and now the chance of bringing our child to us. Darling, don't cry so! I can't bear to see you unhappy." Tenderly he brought her trembling body to him, bending his head to kiss her tenderly on the lips. "In a few short weeks' time this will all be in the past, darling, and we'll be happy together.''

"My mother," she cried, "and Roger!"

"We must persuade the people who have our son to let him go without a fight."

"You know where he is?"

"Your mother has given me the address in Florida. She doesn't think the people will have moved because they had only just bought the house and their business is not far away."

"Do you know our son's name?"

"No, dear, I don't."

The tragedy of it all! Alida wept bitter tears that night, but a few days later, when Darius said she was to accompany him to Florida, she was outwardly composed. Marcelle had been ordered by Roger to pack her bags at once and he had had them taken to the boat. No one had seen her off, and none of them expected ever to see her again.

The house in Florida was in Coral Gables, a beautiful city to the south of Miami. Alida had been there before, but to Darius it was all quite new, the wide boulevards, the other beautifully landscaped thoroughfares, the Spanish and Mediterranean influences of the houses and other buildings. Mainly the wealthy lived there, and when Darius, having located the house where their son was living, stopped the car both he and Alida stared in silence for some considerable time, neither of them inclined to comment.

"I'll drive in," he decided eventually, and the car sped forward along an avenue of glorious cypress trees that ended in a tropical garden ablaze with colour. He stopped the car and they got out, Alida's nerves quivering, her heart beating rapidly. She heard children's laughter, and a man's voice saying,

"Hey, when do I get the ball! Kick it over here, Richard."

A tall, dark-haired boy raced through some shrubs, chasing a football. The two standing there watched as he manoeuvred it with adept side-stepping movements towards the open space beyond which was obviously the ground on which the children were playing. "Get ready, Dad—it's coming—!" The boy stopped and stared, then ran towards them. "Can I help you?" he asked politely. "Do you want my father?"

Neither Darius nor Alida could answer; they merely stared into a bronzed young face, a face of classical strength and beauty. The boy's hair was black, his eyes dark grey, like pewter. Alida noticed his long lean hands, his slender limbs, bronzed and strong. She glanced at Darius. His face was set, immobile.

"Do you want my father, sir?" enquired the boy again, but by this time a tall man had appeared, a man of about thirty-nine years of age, good-looking in a rugged kind of way. "Dad," said the boy before he could speak, "a lady and gentleman have called."

Two more children came running, then stopped to stare inquisitively at the visitors. Alida swallowed; she looked down into the face of her son and bit her lip hard to stop its trembling. One of the children was a boy of about seven years of age, the other a pretty fair-haired girl of about five and a half.

"Are you looking for me?" asked the man with a smile.

Darius said quietly,

"No; I'm afraid we've come into the wrong drive. It's next door we want, I think."

"The Crocksleys'? They're away for three weeks, went yesterday."

"I see. . . . Well, I'm sorry to have troubled you." A pause and then, "It's a charming family you have—This fellow—how old is he?"

"Almost eight. He's big for his age."

"Tall," corrected Darius with a hint of indignation which, later, was to cause both Alida and himself a little amusement. "Not big; there's a difference, you know."

"You're right," laughed the man. "I shall remember the next time." He paused, looking them over, and then his eyes went to the boy, Richard. "He has a look of you," he said to Darius. "Dark hair and eyes."

"Yes. He's not like the others."

The boy had been standing by, one foot resting on the ball.

"I'm adopted," he said with a smile. "Mummy says it was a lucky day when she got me because she couldn't have any children and after I came she had two!"

His father laughed and said that people were not really interested in such things.

"Oh, but they are, very interested." Alida spoke for the first time, marvelling at the lightness of her heart, and the serene calmness that enfolded her, erasing all the nerve-tension she had known since she had got out of bed that morning, knowing the errand she was to make. "I think it's a very happy story, Richard."

"I think so too. You see, I've got a brother and sister to play with— She's a girl, of course, and can't kick the ball very well, but she tries hard, doesn't she, Dad?"

"I can kick the ball!"

"All right," agreed Richard smiling at her, "you kick it very well, Mandy."

"Would you care to come in and have a cup of tea—

or perhaps something stronger?" invited the children's father.

Darius glanced down at Alida. She wanted more than anything to see the children's mother, the woman who had taken her son almost at birth, and yet, paradoxically, she felt she would rather not see her, just in case she was not quite all that Alida hoped she would be. However, fate took a hand, as it had taken a hand so much in her life lately, from the direction of the house a young woman came swinging along towards where the group was standing. Slender and of medium height, and with a smile coming instantly to her lips as Richard ran to her, she was in fact all that Alida could have desired. She wore a plain blue linen dress and white sandals. Her hand came out and Richard slipped his into it, bringing it to his face in the way of a much younger child. Unquestionably there was a strong bond between the mother and her adopted son.

"I don't think we'll stay—but thank you all the same." It was Darius who spoke, telling Alida afterwards that he sensed that she wanted to leave now that she had seen the mother.

"You're very welcome to stay," said the father after quickly explaining to his wife that Darius and Alida had come up the wrong drive.

"Thank you again," smiled Darius, "but we must be on our way." The boy was close and he ruffled his hair. "Keep on like that," he said, "and you'll be a champion footballer one day."

The family stood and watched as Darius and Alida got into the car and drove away. A little while later, in a quiet lane, Darius stopped the car. She leant towards him even before he turned to take her in his arms.

"It's silly to—to cry," she said, "but—but he's so like you...."

"And a little like you, my darling," he whispered, his lips caressing her cheek. "His nature, so kind and gentle. What a happy child he is!"

"Happy and secure. Oh, Darius, I'm so glad we've seen him, and I wouldn't even try to take him away, but—but please bear with me if I talk about him sometimes—and cry...."

A tender smile touched the fine outline of his mouth.

"I'll bear with you, my dearest love, but I shan't let you cry. There's nothing to cry about, is there?"

She shook her head.

"No, Darius, there's nothing to cry about—nothing at all."

He kissed her then, with great tenderness and love.

"There'll be others, my dearest—if you want them, that is. Your wishes are paramount this time, and for always."

She made no answer, but nestled in the sweet haven of his arms, confident of his love and devotion, and confident too that, one day soon, there would be another who would grow up like Richard—fine and sturdy, and dearly loved.

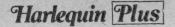

A WORD ABOUT THE AUTHOR

Anne Hampson, one of Harlequin's most prolific writers, is the author of more than thirty Romances and thirty Presents. She holds the distinction of having written the first two Harlequin Presents, in 1973: *Gates of Steel* and *Master of Moonrock*.

Anne is also one of Harlequin's most widely traveled authors, her research taking her to ever new and exotic settings. And wherever she goes she takes copious notes, absorbs all she can about the flora and fauna and becomes completely involved with the people and their customs.

Anne taught school for four years before turning to writing full-time. Her outside interests include collecting antiques, rocks and fossils, and travel is one of her greatest pleasures—but only by ship; like many, she's afraid of flying.

What does she like most? "Sparkling streams, clear starry nights, the breeze on my face. Anything, in fact, that has to do with nature."